THE ABBOT AND THE DWARF

DEREK WEBSTER

The Abbot and the Dwarf

Tales of Wisdom from the Desert

St Paul Publications

Cover illustration by G.V. Faint, The Image Bank

St Paul Publications
Middlegreen, Slough SL3 6BT, United Kingdom
Moyglare Road, Maynooth, Co. Kildare, Ireland

ISBN 085439 416 8
Printed by The Guernsey Press Co. Ltd, Guernsey, C.I.

St Paul Publications is an activity of the priests and brothers of the Society of St Paul who proclaim the Gospel through the media of social communication

Contents

For Wendy

Preface

This little book of stories could be about you. It is also about Abbot Nicholas and his disciple, John the Dwarf. If you come to know them you may spot something curious. They are simple men, poor by worldly standards, yet they try to give something to those they meet. Often they bestow a puzzle whose answer can be found only in living. Sometimes they offer a question which only a particular individual can take up. Occasionally what they give creates a silence. Usually they try to show where there is space, for the lives of those who chance upon them often crave this space.

Although the Abbot and his friend only give empty shells, do these echo a deep-set infinity? Nicholas proffers no more than the merest thread, yet taken up does it lead to Jerusalem's gate? If John simply holds a mirror to those whom they meet, what is reflected back? Is it an image which waits in love beneath life's bustle? Perhaps. Perhaps not.

Stories have strange powers because we bring ourselves to them. They can interpret our lives for us as we live in them. Some stories, in speaking about particular things, seem to speak about many things. Others evoke a mystery which is indistinct, yet which continues to beckon. Like a silent finger, a story can direct attention to what dwells beyond any distance.

The image of the desert, though strange, is a powerful one. Those who have contact with it can sometimes see more clearly and understand their own priorities. The directness with which it speaks of life and death is both refreshing and alarming. John the Dwarf and Abbot Nicholas stand within a rich tradition of fourth century monasticism whose austerity and wisdom, whose commitment and vision continue to draw ordinary people. Setting their parables and stories in this tradition gives an opportunity to speak to contemporary men and women with a particular voice.

On the first reading, a story may entertain a little. When read again and perhaps shared, it may provoke reflection. A third reading, after this pondering, may draw you to inhabit it. Then it becomes a poem which your life sets to music.

Some time ago on vacation from my university, visiting Israel to write what I hoped would be a fairly academic book, something unplanned and unlooked for happened. Instead of going to and fro between libraries and places of historical significance, between scholarly institutions and archaeological sites, I felt drawn to solitary places, to the desert. From time spent alone in such places, all that the Abbot and the Dwarf sing of was born for me. Their stories, however, were not written down until much later. There was a need to understand this 'wilderness experience' and relate it to a context provided by others.

Many have written skilfully and perceptively about solitude, about contemplation and about the desert. Those who spoke particularly to me and helped in the interpretation of this experience, included Thomas Merton and Canon A.M. Allchin, Andrew Louth and the poet R.S. Thomas. Especially nourishing were the translations of Sister Benedicta Ward, Father Norman Russell and Helen Wadell. To these last three, as well as to J.P. Migne, I am especially grateful. Their work has enabled me to use ideas, places and names to give a particular context to these desert tales. Obviously this book is not intended to be a work of scholarship, as theirs are. It simply uses very loosely the lens offered by the Desert Fathers of the fourth century to look in a certain way at the twentieth century. But if this lens has any value, then credit will, almost wholly, be due to those on whose wisdom I have drawn. I happily acknowledge my debt to them and I hope that neither they nor their shades will feel that these little tales diminish their scholarship, and the spirituality from which it so clearly arises. Neither Abbot Nicholas nor John the Dwarf – nor I – would want that.

I am also happy to acknowledge my indebtedness to the priests and people of St Peter's Church, Cleethorpes, who have given me so much over many years, especially Brian and Tom. Like all who teach I find that I am taught continuingly by my University colleagues and students. I thank them all, especially Alan, Mike and Molly. Without the understanding and support of the members of my family this book would never have been started, let alone completed. I am grateful to Ruby for the interest which she has shown in what she called 'her book'; to Wendy and my children – who will know why; and to Andrew Mark, Graham and Marris who, sadly, can never know why. Particular thanks go to Veronica Fraser, Director of Education in the Diocese of Worcester. She gave time to, thought for and encouragement of this book just when it was most needed.

All who try to reflect a Christian spirituality in stories are conscious of the huge debt that they owe to the great religious traditions of the world. Indeed it is often said that there are no new stories. Nevertheless I hope that I have not unwittingly infringed copyright or otherwise used material which others see as their own.

Derek Webster
The University of Hull
Feast of St Cuthbert of Lindisfarne, 1992

MEDITERRANEAN SEA

ALEXANDRIA

LAKE MAREOTIS

NITRIA

CELLIA

WILDERNESS OF SCETE

ARSINOE

RIVER NILE

PISPIR

ANTINOE

EGYPT

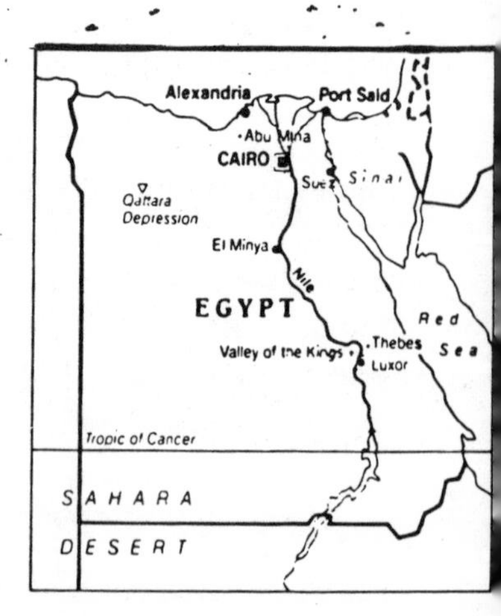

1
Truth

One morning Abbot Nicholas received three visitors. The first approached his small courtyard as the sun was rising and he was breaking his fast with goat's milk and cheese. Dismounting a camel, the traveller left his attendants at the gate and asked permission to enter the cell. It was Biare, a nobleman of Alexandria, dressed in blue silks and the finest linen. When Nicholas had given a greeting and washed his feet, they prayed together and a simple meal was prepared for him and his servants.

Nicholas lived very simply, with his disciple John the Dwarf, in the Nitrian deserts.[1] The credulous said that his holiness was so great that God had granted him the knowledge of all things; the wise respected his humility.

Biare knelt before Nicholas and said:

'Holy Father, give me the truth, I pray.'

For some time Nicholas said nothing. Then stretching out his hand, he took from a bowl a desert rose. Handing the flower to Biare, he blessed him and sent him away.

Before the mid-morning psalm, slaves rested a golden litter at the gate of the courtyard. In it, dressed in red velvet and the richest furs, was Pelusia, a princess from the royal house of Thebes. She asked permission to enter the cell. Again Nicholas greeted her, washed her feet and prayed with her. After this John brought food for them.

Pelusia knelt before Nicholas and said:

'Holy Father, show me the truth, I pray.'

For some time Nicholas said nothing. Then leaning forwards, he breathed upon her, blessed her and sent her away.

***

I am small and despised,
Yet I do not forget thy precepts.

(Ps 119:141)

At the time for the mid-day psalms, a frail and elderly man, dressed only in the coarsest of rags, limped to the gate and begged to drink from the well in the courtyard. He had been the market-sweeper in Alexandria, but was now too old to labour. Nicholas came out to him and embraced him in greeting. Bringing him into the cell from the burning of the sun, he washed his feet. Then they celebrated the Synaxis.[2]

May these earthly crumbs from bread, be to us
that immortal wheat which is His own Body.
May these drops of wine be to us drink from
that immortal vine which is His own Blood.

He was given a simple meal, after which he knelt before Nicholas and said:

'Holy Father, answer me one question, I pray.
What is truth?'

Nicholas' piercing eyes looked with deep love upon Asclas the market-sweeper of Alexandria. And he raised him gently. They sat in close talk. The hours passed. John attending to his duties brought them water and plain bread, but they seemed not to notice. It was towards evening when Nicholas blessed the old man and he departed.

***

I have chosen the way of truth...
How sweet are thy words to my taste...
The unfolding of thy words gives light;
  it imparts understanding to the simple.

(Ps 119:30,103,130)[3]

After they had said the night psalms, John, sitting quietly by the Abbot, said:

'Holy Father, the three guests asked the same question. Why did you deal differently with each?'

Nicholas, with the wisp of a smile, replied:

'Were we really inhospitable, my friend? Our guests took what they were able to receive.

Biare thinks that truth is like a goblet encrusted with gems which he can possess. This thought traps him.[4] I gave him what can be possessed. Soon his rose will die and then he will understand more.

Pelusia thinks that truth is shown like the fanning tails of her peacocks. This thought traps her. I gave her what cannot be shown. Soon she will understand more.

Asclas knows that one ever asks about truth, for the pilgrimage from birth to death is set within it. This thought frees him.

Truth is both the beginning and the end of his quest.
It ever lifts and abides within him.
It longingly draws and always encompasses him.
It inhabits the sweepings of the market place.
Very soon now he will find it fulfilled in his dying.'

John pondered a while before asking:

'Then each of us is a moment in the other's truth?'

Nicholas looked at him and beyond him. He said quietly:

'As now. And perhaps forever.'

> With my whole heart I seek thee...
> I have laid up thy words in my heart...
>
> (Ps 119:10,11)

2
Silence

Travelling alone on the long journey from Scete,[5] Abbot Nicholas returned to his desert cell just before the time for evening prayers. His disciple John the Dwarf greeted him with an embrace and washed the dust of the Nitrian wastes from his feet. Then together they said their psalms.

> He will deliver you from the snare of the fowler
> and from the deadly pestilence;
> he will cover you with his pinions,
> and under his wings you will find refuge.
>
> (Ps 91:3,4)

Afterwards Nicholas ate the bread and figs prepared for him by his disciple. But he spoke no words. John served him for two days and save for the biddings of their prayers, his Master said nothing.

***

At sunrise on the third day he called John to him. He asked him this question:

'My son, what destroys silence?'

John sat quietly at his feet and pondered for some time. Then he replied:

> 'My Lord, as the clear air of the morning
> is not seen until the smoking fire has died,
> so do evil affections blot out that silence within
> which Holy Wisdom may be received by the heart.'

Nicholas agreed and John continued:

'The Holy One has set many caverns of deepest
darkness within which to meet His disciples.
The noise of their knowledge can drive out
the silence within which His Glory is set.'

The Abbot gently smiled and John went on:

'My Master, if there are two rivers from the same spring, the one that branches into a thousand channels has no worth. Its waters are too meagre for the farmer. The one which remains single he rejoices in. So do the thousand attachments of this life slay that silence in which the singleness of pure faith is throned.'

***

Nicholas asked John a second question:

'My son, what truth lies in silence?'

John thought for a very long time before answering. Eventually picking up a fig, he said:

'Each seed of the fig holds the secret of a tree in the silence of its heart.'

The Master nodded and waited for him to speak again.

Then the dwarf saw the sun's rays pierce the cell's darkness and he said:

'The light of day shows all things. But as the eye in seeing looks not upon itself, so the light in showing is silent of itself.'

Nicholas accepted this but motioned him to continue. John however paused. Finally he said:

'That life which quickens surging
Leviathan,[6]
The sweet honeysuckle,
And me,
Is given, serves and is taken
In dark silence.'

***

The Master gently pointed John to sit with him.

Silence is a lonely stranger amid the profanity of noise.
Stand at the sea's edge and see her come toward you.
Watch a woman walk the darkened way, it is she.
She is the mourner at a forgotten grave.
She is the unbearable ecstasy of each new spring.
She is the innocence of children in play.

Across the empty sands,
Silence brings her gifts to all.

She completes all things.
She brings to sleep the wholeness of death.
She gives to dreams the fullness of prophecy.
She changes the day of His Rising to eternal life.
Only she may bend the sun's ray to Heavenly Light.
Only she may change Holy Scripture into Divine Wisdom.
She shapes earthly sense to the dearest love of Christ.

She speaks without sound.
Does she say:
As the sand storm drives a desert mouse
And swirling waters spin the fish.
So eddies human life?

Does she say:
There is no satiety, no final fulfilment for
The strings are discordant and colours dim
Until His Coming to bestow new being?

For a while neither spoke. Then the Abbot began to say:

'Your speaking has many pearls…'

John quietly interrupted:

'But you have given me the necklace.'

They sat together in the quietness until it was time for the psalms and prayers.

Thy way was through the sea,
Thy path through the great waters;
yet thy footprints were unseen.
(Ps 77:19)

So it was that John the Dwarf learned that He who is Truth is girded with silence.

3
Vocation

Yet thou art he who took me from the womb;
thou didst keep me safe upon my mother's breasts.

(Ps 22:9)

As Abbot Nicholas and John the Dwarf intoned their early morning psalms, five travellers arrived at the gate of their courtyard. They were on the long journey to Arsinoe.[7] The two holy men saluted their visitors in the traditional way and then set a simple meal of salt-bread, dates and fresh water before them. Afterwards they told their stories to the Abbot and asked for a blessing. Strangely in early life, all had desired to follow the purity of the desert life. Yet a curious circumstance had prevented each of them from taking this holy path.

The first to speak was a tall, elderly man. He wore a long robe trimmed with fur and was called Sopatrus. Skilled in the arts of medicine and the knowledge of herbs, he said with deep seriousness:

> 'As a young man my city was ravaged by a barbarian army. Many died or were wounded. Sickness and disease began to grow. I wished to meet the suffering of my family and the poor. So I studied the arts of medicine.
> Thus, I did not follow the most holy path.'

Chomas spoke second. He was a much younger man and wore the rough clothes of a carpenter.

> 'And I fell in love with a godly woman. We married and God has blessed our lives with six daugh-

ters. We match our living to that of the Lord's disciples. We labour, we give alms and we sing the Lord's praises whether He gives us joy or sorrow.

Thus I did not follow the most holy path.'

A rather round man in a richly embroidered cloak spoke next. His name was Doulas and he was a lawyer.

'As a youth my father was falsely imprisoned. Visiting him I was broken at the plight of the weak and the corruption of judges. I studied the law and the art of advocacy to plead for innocent captives.

Thus did I not follow the most holy path.'

The fourth man was called Sarmatas the Wise. Over his stooped back he wore the gown of a teacher. Speaking slowly he said:

'I was raised in Alexandria[8] and was taught by the wise monk Ammonius. He showed me how deeply ignorant of the Holy Gospels the people of our city were. I determined to bring the light of God's Wisdom to them.

Thus I put aside the most holy path.'

Megethius was the final guest. A quietly spoken man of mature years, he wore the clothes of a merchant and said:

'Unworthy as I am, God has allowed me to know His Presence each day.

I see Him:
in the cunning of a craftsman's hands,
in the herbs of the field,
and in the bittern's sad cry.
He is given:
in coolness of water and heat of flame,
in love of parent and obedience of child.

Because of this, His gift to me,
  I put aside the most holy path.'

Abbot Nicholas talked for some time privately with each man. Then he blessed them as they left to continue their journey.

***

Following the afternoon prayers, Nicholas asked his disciple:

'John, the lives of our guests,
do they follow the most holy path?'

The Dwarf answered quickly:

'I think that they do, though it happens without their know-ledge. For the most holy way lies within the soul, not among the sands of Nitria.

Sopatrus in binding the wounds of the sick,
  binds His wounds.

Chomas by taking the path of discipleship,
  walks the 'Way'.

Doulas in committing himself to what is right,
  is himself made righteous.

Sarmatas in teaching the Holy Scriptures,
  lives close to the High One.

And Megethius in receiving insight and visions
  abides in His Very Presence for...'

Then John stopped. Puzzled he said:

'But this you know already, Master. It is your teaching.'

His eyes laughed as he said to the Abbot:

'Why do you ask me?
Can the grasshopper teach the lark to sing?
Do they not walk in the most holy path?'

Nicholas looked long into the desert horizon before saying softly:

'The most holy path is what He sets for each of His children.
Some will shear and some will sweep.
Some will sing and some will kneel in silent prayer.
Always the good may drive out what is better.

Only our visitors and the Father know if His call to each of them is betrayed by a holy thing.'

Before John set out the meal, they said the psalms for the hour.

Trust in the Lord, and do good...
Be still before the Lord, and wait patiently for him.
(Ps 37:3,7)

4
Death

So teach us to number our days
that we may get a heart of wisdom.

(Ps 90:12)

It was at the weekly Synaxis with their brothers from cells in that part of Nitria that Abbot Nicholas and John the Dwarf heard the news. Sisois the Good of Pispir,[9] the counsellor of princes, had died. He who had mocked the world and spent a lifetime of death for love was no longer with them. Nicholas pondered privately and silently.

His friendship with Sisois had a beginning at the Imperial Court in Rome, for both were sons of powerful tribunes, favourites of the Emperor. Nicholas had long ago repented of the circuses, the cruelty and the abuse, as no doubt he reflected, had the dearest friend of his youth. Recalling the many hours spent in helping Sisois read the Pagan's Texts and write their Grammar, his mind smiled. Sisois the Mule, their teacher Democritus used to say, while he waited impatiently for his pupil to grasp the ancient learning. How right he was, thought Nicholas, for the mule also carries great burdens. And within his tiny cell in the wastes of Pispir, Sisois the Good had borne, for more than fifty years, the weight of the problems of the highest born.

The Abbot remembered their parting as young men, to live in the desert with different masters. He had embraced Sisois saying:

'At the return of the sun, when it is time for the first

prayer, I shall ask the Holy One to protect you. And this I will do each morning of my life.'

Sisois had returned his embrace and holding him had said:

> 'My friend, you, who so young, know all of the letters of the book of wisdom, know this also. At the appearance of the evening star, I shall ask the Holy One to protect you. And this I will do each evening of my life – and in Paradise.'

* * *

When the Dwarf and his Master returned from the Synaxis they found three monks waiting for them at the gate of the courtyard. They were disciples of Sisois the Good and they had journeyed through the cruel barrenness of the Nitrian desert, bearing a gift for the Abbot, soul friend of their Master.

After a quiet greeting, Nicholas washed their feet, while John prepared a simple meal of cheese and olives with fresh water from the well. They attended to their prayers and the psalms for that time.

> Do not hide thy face from me in the day of my tress!
> I am like a vulture of the wilderness...
> I eat ashes like bread, and mingle tears with my drink...
> My days are like an evening shadow; I wither away like grass.
>
> (Ps 102:2,6,9,11)

They ate in silence. Grief gave pain. Then the three spoke to Nicholas by turn. The youngest, Xoius, a lad taken by Sisois from slavery, said:

'Father Abbot, my Master's absence is greater than
I can bear. How may I renew my spirit?'

Nicholas gently embraced him and said:

'Let those things which brought him joy, echo
his being.
Look for the brightest star of evening.
Watch for the geese on their homeward flight.
See the smile of the jonquil's beauty.
Such things will refresh your spirit.'

Next was Hierax, a brother in his prime. He said:

'Father Abbot, my Master's absence is greater than
I can bear. How may I live again?'

As he knelt at the holy man's knees, Nicholas quietly took his arm and spoke softly to him.

'Let those things which he began in his living,
your living continue.
Where there are shadows in friends' lives,
shed light.
Where there is sadness, give joy.
Where hurt, bring balm.
Thus can you live and continue to serve Sisois.'

The oldest, Spyridon, spoke last. Prostrating himself, he wept:

'Father Abbot, my Master's absence is greater than
I can bear. How may I find him again?'

Nicholas knelt at his side and placed a hand on his head.

'Sisois the Good abides in a greater light than we can know and stands in a deeper love than we can conceive. But you may find him again by loving what he loved. So continue to study the Holy Scriptures, mark the hours of prayer each day and night, share in the Feast of the Lord, distribute alms to the needy and pray with the dying. Serve your Master Christ with all your strength and you will serve Sisois.'

With provisions from John and the blessing of Nicholas, the three began the long journey to their own small monastery at Pispir.

***

Before the night prayer, Nicholas bade John open the gift. It was a short staff. At its top Sisois had carved some tiny Greek letters. John read them to his Master:

AND IN PARADISE

He looked at Nicholas who said to him:

'It means my son, that Sisois the Mule has blown out the candle. Though his night has gone and his day now come, yet he remembers us.'

He smiled as in their psalms and prayers they gave thanks for all that God had wrought through the life of Sisois the Good.

My heart is steadfast, O God, my heart is steadfast!
I will sing and make melody!
Awake my soul! Awake, O harp and lyre!
I will awake the dawn!

(Ps 57:7,8)

5
Theologians

Be still, and know that I am God.
(Ps 46:10)

It was in the season of the hot winds that the Bishop of Alexandria and his two chaplains Thomas and Theon passed through the Nitrian deserts. For three days they rested with Abbot Nicholas and John the Dwarf sharing in their prayers, the psalms and the Synaxis. They were returning from some weeks attendance at the Ecumenical Council. On the last evening, the meal being finished, they spoke to their hosts of this great meeting.

Thomas and Theon, not yet in middle age, were learned men. Schooled in philosophy and Scripture, they knew both Latin and Greek. But, as the first followed the apophatic way and the second the kataphatic, they were quickly in dispute.[10]

Thomas talked of the Most High and drew that dark abyss which no bridge could span, between what men and women say of Him and what He is. He quoted from the earliest Fathers of the faith. Countless were the times he mentioned the Gospels. And his reasoning looked to the mystics as its masters. He finished with the words:

> 'Thus it is that we can never know the Highest and Most Holy, for He is beyond all thinking.'

Theon also talked of God. He began with the words, 'To the contrary…' and set a reverse argument. He painted those ways in which creation echoed the love of God. And he found those human images which carried a dim analogy of His Being. His words too were long. His citations were many. And his logic had Aristotle as its master. He concluded with the words:

> 'Thus it is that we may know the Most High and approach Him in our thinking.'

Their disputation was lengthy. The good Bishop and the holy Abbot, both with half-closed eyes, listened in prayerful silence. Ideas circled in the head of John the faithful disciple, like an angry Egyptian dog chasing its tail. The Bishop finally called 'Amen'. He told his chaplains to make ready for a departure after their first prayers the following morning. John prepared food for them and filled their flasks from the well. As he did so, he saw that the Bishop and Nicholas were in serious and private conversation together.

***

For the three days after their leaving, John's spirit was deeply disturbed. In his wisdom the Abbot asked nothing of him and spoke little. Finally, on the fourth day, the Dwarf came to Nicholas. He knelt before him and said:

> 'Master, release me from my vows that I may spend my years in study and know God through the path of knowledge.'

Nicholas, taking his arm, walked with him among the sands.

> 'Theon's words are true, my son. God may be known. Does not Blessed John record the Christ's very words to Philip: "He who has seen me has seen the Father"?
>
> (Jn 14:9)

Thomas' words are also true. God may not be known. Does not the wise prophet Isaiah say: "For my thoughts are not your thoughts... For as the heavens are higher than the earth, so are... my thoughts than your thoughts".

(Is 55:8,9)

The Bishop's chaplains have much knowledge. Yet they lack wisdom.'

John, unhappy and confused, said:

'Will my Lord explain this to me?'

'You know it already, John.

Why does the darting swift not teach her young
of the summer's breeze?
Or the crocus not speak to her neighbours
of the shining of the sun?
Why do the great dragons of the sea not dispute
about the ocean's deeps?'

John immediately replied:

'Because knowledge of these things is already set within their very natures.'

And as what had imprisoned his spirit was broken, he laughed and said:

'And so do men and women know God.'

***

As Nicholas walked with his disciple back to their cell, he said:

'Look for the Holy One and you will not find Him.
Not an object, He gives meaning to all objects.
Not in any place, He establishes all places.

Not in any creature, He sustains all creatures.
Prior to the idea of proof, He lies beyond any conclusion
He is no further away from you than your life.
You will only bind Him by your love.'

Then the Abbot's eyes shone with mirth. Laughing he said:

'And in ignorance of this simple truth you would leave me to make my own cheese and draw my own water?
Let John the Dwarf learn that wisdom beyond thinking is only found in loving.

On their return, the good Bishop will teach this to his chaplains.

Theon is appointed to bind the wounds of the sick in the great prison of Alexandria. Thomas is given the task of washing the bodies of the dead in the infirmary for the poor.

May these acts of mercy bring wisdom to their learning.
For as King Solomon the Wise saith:
...the Lord gives wisdom;
from his mouth comes... understanding.'
(Prov 2:6)

6
Pagans

Behold, I will lift up my hand to the nations.
(Is 49:22)

To visit the great monastery of Alexandria, Abbot Nicholas and John the Dwarf travelled for six days through the Nitrian wastes. Close to their destination they took the last night's shelter in the courtyard of an inn. With other guests too poor to afford the coin for straw, they huddled round the common fire. After some time, John noticed three men withdraw from the circle. Fearing robbers, he slowly placed his hand on his staff and watched closely.

The first man was naked save for a loincloth. Moving to a corner of the courtyard, he took from his bag a clay statue. With great care he placed it on a log and then, taking a desert marigold in each hand, he danced slowly and quietly around it, murmuring:

> 'Even as a Beloved Guest enters a house, so do you great Goddess arrayed in black apparel, come with rest... Watch over the valleys and lofty peaks with your thousand eyes... Enfold your creatures and to all children grant safe lodging this holy night...'

The second man tied a medallion around his forehead. Then he set a picture in the earth and garlanding it with coloured ribbons, prostrated himself before it singing:

> 'Great God from Whom the sun rises and in Whom it sinks for refreshment, preserve us in our sleeping... blind the eyes of the snake, darken the sight

> of the wolf and entrap the thief in his own snare... Inhabit the deep cavern of my heart as a Waiting Friend...'

The third man lit a small candle and placing a white cloth on his head, sat before the flame whispering the softest of chants.

> 'Thou who art in all Thy creation, whose compassion does not forget Thy smallest creature, grant me that understanding which knows Thee in the moonlight as it plays upon a thousand waters, as it cools the weary, guards the sleeping and bathes the hearts of the prayerful.'

'Our brothers remind us that it is time for the nightly office', whispered the Abbot to John. Then withdrawing from the circle, together they prayed:

> That God would hide them under the shadow of
> His wing,
> protect them from the terror that crept by night
> and the arrows that sped by day.
> That He would bless their brethren,
> forgive the wicked,
> relieve the needy,
> console the dying,
> and bring all His children by the waters of comfort to
> His Safe Pasture.

***

John said to the Abbot the following morning as they entered the outskirts of Alexandria:

> 'Master, why did you call those who were pagan worshippers, our brothers? In the wickedness of their idolatry are not they the sons of Belial, as we are the sons of Light?'

Nicholas took time to answer his chosen disciple.

'John, is not the hen a mother to all her chicks?
Is not each face of the jacinth of equal beauty?
The snow that falls on the cedars of Lebanon, does it not refresh each tree with the same coolness?

So is God a loving Father to all His children.
So are we these children, and thus brothers and sisters each to the other.'

Still puzzled the Dwarf asked:

'But Master, is it not the Son who is Lord of all Truth? Gives He not this Truth to us?'

The Abbot answered:

'My son, there is truth in your words but not your understanding.

First remember this.
Children hold within, like a seed, all their potency.
Parents see only in part and cannot know the grace they will show as life waxes.
So Truth that is unbounded is indeed given to us.
But we, bounded, understand but its smallest part.
By the mercy of God, its wholeness will appear when this body, which is dust, puts on that body which is heavenly.

Second, remember this.
Light is one and is not divided in itself.
In what place and time, with what people and practice it is seen, it is the same Light.
The Lord Christ, who is the Universal Word,[11] speaks with a multitude of accents, and through time draws around Himself the cloak of many histories.'

So John the Dwarf learned of the Father's love for men and women who, following the light within themselves, unknowingly walk the Way given to their times.

Thus he learned that Heraclitus of Ephesus and Philo the Jew,[12] the seekers of India and the sages of China, were kin to him and beloved of the Most Holy.

The Master and his disciple sat a little apart from the main highway to say their morning psalms.

> Praise the Lord!… praise him in the heights!…
> Kings of the earth and all peoples,
> princes and all rulers of the earth…
> Let them praise the name of the Lord,
> for his name alone is exalted…
>
> (Ps 148:1,11,12)

7
Desert

In the day of my trouble I seek the Lord;
in the night my hand is stretched out...
my soul refuses to be comforted.
(Ps 77:2)

Walking along the avenue of cypresses to the gate of the great monastery of Alexandria, a very agitated young man joined himself to Abbot Nicholas and John the Dwarf. When he learned they were monks he drew them aside, anxious to tell of his attempt at the contemplative life in the wilderness of Judaea. The son of a wealthy wine-merchant, Pambo the Tall had encountered a hermit who persuaded him to put aside his inheritance, change his tunic of fine linen for a shirt of coarse cloth and live the Holy Way in a desert cell.

He intoned:

'In that barrenness beyond my hut,
I was scourged by the wind, burned by the sun
and tormented by the sand.
In a dryness beyond all prayer, I was bitten by
doubt, enslaved by illusion and shocked by
temptation.
In my illness I was visited by grotesque frogs
and hideous birds, fiendish creatures
and loathsome worms.
And then, mounted on a scarlet beast with seven
heads and ten horns, the harlot of Babylon
came to claim me.[13]
Her beauty was that of the Shulammite.[14]
Her eyes were the pools of Heshbon,[15]

The tresses of her hair, a royal tapestry,
The neck, an ivory tower.
Her breasts were twin fawns of a gazelle
browsing among the lily fields.
Her navel was a rounded goblet filled
with the rarest of strong wines.

Nightly she visited me. Nightly, this demon without substance goaded emissions.[16] So I could not share in the great Synaxis. My brothers urged me to fasting. And I drank but a small cup of water each day, that there should be no excess of fluid in the darkness. Still the nightly terror came. Driven to greater fasting I drank but half a cup of water in each day. As I grew weaker she came without her veils. Her flesh became more white, her breath more honeyed, her thighs more sweetly perfumed. In deepest anguish, seeking to transcend my nature and not fall further into pollution, I drank nothing for three days.

I was dying when my father found me and brought me home again.'

* * *

Even in the warm morning sun, beads of sweat appeared to tell of the dread that still lived within him and twisted his life. Nicholas bade John go ahead to the monastery and inform the Abbot of their coming, secure their lodging and beg a little food and drink. Then he gently led Pambo to a quiet place in a grove of magnolia trees. There they talked in great seriousness. After some time John returned with provisions, but they hardly noticed so attentive were they to each other's words. He sat a little way off and kept the psalms of each hour for the three of them.

Why go I mourning
because of the oppression of the enemy?
As with a deadly wound in my body,
my adversaries taunt me...
Why are you cast down, O my soul?...
Hope in God.

(Ps 42:910,11)

Towards evening, Pambo knelt before Nicholas, received his blessing and returned to his father's house, his spirit fully restored.

***

Leaning on John's shoulder for support so great was his fatigue, the holy Abbot said to his disciple:

'Tell me, my son:
Should the lily be sad that it is not a rose,
Or the fox that it is not a lion?'

John shook his head. And with a faint smile he added to himself:

'Nor John that he is not the holiest abbot in all deserts.'

Nicholas went on:

'Nor need Pambo regret that he will not be an anchorite.
Tell me also, is not the desert,
joy as well as pain,
a garden as well as a wilderness,
a cradle as well as a tomb?'

Again John nodded.

'He whose being does not feel each side of this truth will never live in the deserts', said Nicholas, slowly adding:

'His brothers were without understanding of him. They were fierce, when they needed to be gentle. In their ignorance, it was they who gave the demon her strength. The wisest Fathers of our Church do not look upon an emission in sleep as sinful but as a natural excrescence.'

They walked for a while in silence. Each had his own thoughts.

'Tell me further, my son, where is the desert?'

John answered:

'Is it not in the soul, Master?
The monk is in a desert as he walks by a sea's shore
or travels a city's streets,
as he stands at a mountain peak
or feasts with his friends.
Did not Pambo confuse the rocks and the sand for the desert?'

'Truly he did,' said the Abbot, and went on:
'Why do men go to the desert?'

'To so live in the Presence of God, Holy Father,
that they may be present to the world.
In solitude one is united to all,
in all and for all.'[17]

***

Knocking at the monastery gate, John said merrily:

'There are many in this city, Father Abbot, who will give thanks that you returned Pambo the Tall to the business of selling wines.'

The Abbot joined his disciple's laughter and commented:

'Better a good wine-seller than a bad monk.'

8
Solitude

How lovely is thy dwelling place,
O Lord of hosts!...
Even the sparrow finds a home,
and the swallow a nest for herself,
where she may lay her young, at thy altars.
(Ps 84:1,3)

During their stay in the great monastery of Alexandria, Abbot Nicholas and John the Dwarf were served by Simon the Deacon, youngest of all the brothers.

'He ministers to you, that you may minister to him and to me', said the wise Abbot Bessarion.

Sitting with his friends in the small library of the monastery, he had listened warmly as they brought him greetings from his many brothers in Nitria. He then spoke to them of his burdens, of the persecutions in Alexandria and of the monks whose souls were in his charge. As he told them of Simon he spoke more hesitantly:

'He was brought to us when a stripling by his slave and devoted tutor, the aged Hyllas of Athens. Only they survived the pillage of the lad's family villa, the firing of all their fields by brigands from the western deserts. Set on the shores of Lake Mareotis,[18] his beautiful estate was razed and all his kin murdered.

As the Holy One granted that Job should be tested, so has He girdled Simon the Deacon with His fire.'

The Abbot, speaking very deliberately, told what had

been known only to Hyllas. Simon carried within himself an infirmity of the blood from his ancestors, which would prevent him reaching twenty years. Bessarion paused, then said:

'That the final darkness now reaches towards him, he does not discern, though Hyllas knows the pattern of it. As a father tenderly loves his son and is loved in return by him, so is the affection that each holds for the other and the service each gives to the other.

But another phantom claws Brother Simon. He holds it to himself unable yet to give it shape in words or thought. Subtle of mind and brave of heart, he has hidden it from all. Only Hyllas and I have perceived it. This phantom brings a deep sadness to him. But its nature is veiled from us. In order to receive your wisdom Hyllas asked that Simon be appointed to serve you.'

***

Well-favoured by God, Simon the Deacon was holy in spirit, learned in mind and fresh in looks. He attended John and Nicholas diligently. Each perceived his goodness and his sadness. After some days had passed Abbot Nicholas asked to speak with Hyllas. For two hours they talked intently together. Then he asked Bessarion and John to come to the library and sent Hyllas to bring the lad also to him. Arriving, he knelt before them all. Abbot Nicholas gently bade him raise his humbled head and lift his eyes to them.

'My son,' he said, 'the dart which gives your pain, can it be drawn by others?'

'My Lord, the battle I fight is single for my adversary is as yet unknown.'

But the shining blueness of his eyes reached for help.

The long silence which followed was at last broken by Nicholas who spoke very quickly, even sharply.

'Very well, as Jacob wrestled alone, so must you.[19] Let us now talk of holy things. You know there are brothers who live in great communities as here in Alexandria, and others whom the Lord calls to a solitary life. Which are the better?'

'My Lord, is the jonquil more lovely than the crocus?'

'Do you know the solitary life?' asked Nicholas.

'No, my Lord. I was given to this monastery as a boy.'

'No matter, guess your answers to my questions. What is false solitude?'

'As a thief flees from the judge, so do men fly from the Holy One within their hearts. False solitude is that sanctuary of inner blindness within which they set their idols to self.'

'How is false solitude seen, my son?'

'It is seen, Holy Father, as a maze of mirrors which constantly reflects the self to the self. What has no substance taunts what equally has no substance.'

The Abbot regarded the young man very closely. For he answered without stratagems of thought to deceive or impress, but quickly from the nakedness of his soul.

'Now what is true solitude?' asked Nicholas.

'My Lord, as the Jabbok[20] seeks the Jordan, the true soul seeks the Holy One at its heart. Solitude is that green valley in which the Father knows His children and they Him.'

'Your last question. From what does solitude separate?'

'From nothing, my Lord. It locks the gate against none. The soul withdraws to the desert the more to be with others. The solitary is in love with all.'

'As you love all', said Nicholas very quietly, but beginning to smile.

Then he raised Simon. Laughing a little, he embraced him. As he understood the young man wept in joy, for his great sadness was lifted.

'Now the young eagle may fly to the mountain's top', said Nicholas to Hylas.

In this way Simon the Deacon discovered his vocation to solitude. Accompanied only by his faithful servant, teacher and friend, Hyllas of Athens, he left the great monastery of Alexandria for a desert cell in Scete.

As they departed Nicholas watched the care which Hyllas showed to Simon. Turning to John and Bessarion he said sadly:

'Now the swallow hath found a house where she may lay her young, even His altar.'

The three monks then prayed their psalms together.

My soul thirsts for God, for the living God.
When shall I come and behold the face of God?

(Ps 42:2)

9
Harlot

John the Dwarf and Abbot Nicholas were saying the mid-morning psalms with their brothers.

> O Lord, why dost thou cast me off?
>   Why dost thou hide thy face from me?
> Afflicted and close to death from my youth up,
>   I suffer thy terrors; I am helpless.
>
> (Ps 88:14,15)

The porter waited until the worship was finished. Then he asked Abbot Nicholas to come to the gate where a common girl of the city awaited him. This was during the second month that they were guests of Abbot Bessarion in the Monastery of Alexandria.

She asked Nicholas to go with her to the House of Fantasies where her mistress was dying. Taking John, he went to that infamous place. It was a fine villa with white marble pillars at its entrance and was set in a wooded park.

***

The rich velvet curtains were slowly drawn aside by two eunuchs. Egregia, now a very old woman, lay on a couch of silken cushions, each with golden tassels. Great tapestries, cunningly woven in finest thread, guarded tall walls. Through the open shutter, a breeze made the air of her room heavy with the scent of hyacinth and early flowering lilac. The peacocks in the garden sang a shrill wail for the passing of one who, in the years of her youth, was a delight for the wealthiest merchants of Alexandria.

> Her eyes which once were turtle doves, flitting in the apple tree, moved sightless in yellow pools.
> She, whose scent was an enclosed Spring garden, with breath as honey and sweetest spice, had become dung.
> That loveliness which was the sun in the rising dawn and dew on the morning rose, was twisted bone, leprous skin.

Nicholas, embracing her with a kiss, bade all others leave save John, whom he set to guard the door of her chamber. The Dwarf watched as his beloved Master, nearly as frail as she whom he comforted, listened to Egregia's confession. She whispered to his ear, as he knelt on the floor beside her couch. A spiritual suitor, he sought that love which he knew God had bestowed upon her and hidden in her soul. John noticed that as he listened, he was startled. With surprise, with disbelief, he spoke to her. Then he nodded slowly and absolved her of all of her sins, remembered and unremembered.

Still kneeling by her side, he offered the psalms and prayers for the dying.

> Thou makest his beauty to consume away,
> like as it were a moth fretting a garment…
> Thou hast taken me up and thrown me away.
>
> As far as the east is from the west,
> so far does he remove our transgressions from us:
> as the heavens are high above the earth,
> so great is his steadfast love.
>
> (Ps 39:12[21] 102:10; Ps 103:12,11)

He stayed far into the evening until all breath left her. The shrieking of the peacocks ceased and women came to wash her body. Nicholas spoke to them.

'Set aside what others have laid out for her burial. Do not wrap her in an embroidered cape or girdle of fur. Do not place upon her head the ruby tiara nor around her arms the gold of serpent bangles. Dress her only in the linen set aside for virgins. Bring her to the monastery at the sixth hour placing upon her white lilies, sweet jasmine and a spray from the myrtle tree.'[22]

***

As they walked back to the monastery through the darkness, the good Abbot sensed John's confusion and anxiety.

'Three things trouble me, Holy Father. They are the kiss with which you greeted Egregia the harlot; her burial as a virgin; and her coronation with the symbols of purity and love.'

The Abbot smiled.

'Will you reprove me, John, for greeting my friend with an embrace? So very long ago now as children we played together at the Imperial Court in Rome. When my foot bled she dressed it, when my head hurt she kissed it, and when life was sad she brought joy.

So lovely was her youthfulness, so gracious her movement, so rare was her beauty, so soft her body and sweet her temper, that she was stolen for ransom by marauding Goths. The price failed. Sold then for sixty pieces of silver to the Temple of Astarte[23] in Alexandria, her life remained for ever gripped by the greed of men and their lusts. Like the nameless concubine of Bethlehem, in the nineteenth chapter of the Holy Book of God's Judges, Egregia's body was broken and given to many without her consenting.[24]

Confession is to God alone, my son. But outside it she said that, though her body was grievously violated in ways of which it is not permitted for us to speak, in spirit she was a pure virgin. At each pollution, through all the years, she prayed for her persecutors. She may wear the white of the true virgin, for such in her heart she has ever been.

At the end she asked God to forgive those who stole her and exercised their will upon her, binding her to defilement. It is fitting that symbols of pure love be placed around Egregia's corpse.'

As they arrived back at the monastery the first fingers of light showed in the sky. Nicholas finished by saying:

'She knew that the presence of the Father never left her.'

Waiting for the sleepy porter to open the gate, John and the Abbot said the first psalm of the new day.

If I ascend to heaven, thou art there!
If I make my bed in Sheol, thou art there!...
If I say, 'Let only darkness cover me,
    and the light about me be night,'
even the darkness is not dark to thee,
the night is bright as the day;
    for darkness is as light with thee.

(Ps 139:8,11,12)

10
Wisdom

The fool says in his heart,
'There is no God'...
God looks down from heaven...
to see if there are any that are wise,
that seek after God.
They have all fallen away...
...under their lips is the poison of vipers.
(Ps 53:1,2,3; Ps 140:3)

Finishing their morning psalms, John and Nicholas prepared to visit the great School of Rhetoric in Alexandria. Its scholars had invited the Abbot to debate with them. On their way to the place of meeting, Nicholas paused to speak to a beggar, whose crippled and misshapen body drew his and John's special sympathy.

'We have no alms to give, for we are poor as you.'

'Give me time?' he asked them.

So it was that they sat by Paul the Beggar in the dust of the road that leads to the fish market.

'Tell me friend, of those things for which you give thanks in your life', said Nicholas.

'Why Father, they are those things which bring joy to all.

Of flowers I love the rose and anemone most.
The rose because its thorns remind me that I have fallen from grace and its beauty that I might regain Paradise.
The anemone because at evening of the saddest day it burst forth from the Cross' root, weeping with His Blood.

Of trees I love the holly and myrtle most.
The holly because it was the wood that tortured the
Blessed One, and wrought our salvation.
The myrtle because Zachary says from its groves the
Lord set out to win the Gentiles.[25]

Of animals I love most the hart and the pelican.
The first because he seeks the water-brooks as we
seek the love of God.
The second, because loving her young she pierces
her breast to feed them with her blood. So doth
Christ feed those who love him.

Of people I love most my parents, my friends and
my enemies.
My parents because maid Mary the Virgin loved the
Blessed Joachim and Anna.
My friends because the Lord loved his disciples
to the end.
My enemies because my Master Christ bids me
so to do.'

Then each asked a blessing of the other. And John the Dwarf in the silence of his spirit first laughed then wept, as he watched two old and frail men, sitting in the mud and filth of the common highway, bless each other. The world in its busyness passed by, seeing nothing.

***

John the Dwarf sat on the floor behind the students' benches, as his Master walked towards the teachers at the centre of the debating chamber. While the preliminaries were taking place he said his psalms.

For lo, the wicked bend the bow,
they have fitted their arrow to the string,
to shoot in the dark at the upright in heart.

(Ps 11:2)

It seemed as if the frail figure of Nicholas would be overwhelmed by words as each scholar stood up to demonstrate his disbelief in God. But he answered them by turn, with a depth of thought which disguised itself in words of simplicity and poetry. Though respecting their doubt, he tried to show the weaknesses in their arguments and the assumptions in their terms.

The wise teachers laughed as Nicholas told them of the foolishness of the youngest monks and the eccentricities of the most ancient in the cells of Nitria.

They listened intently when he spoke of that Universal Truth, called the Word of God, in the Gospel of Blessed John; of His Presence in Abraham and Moses; and of His Habitation in the knowledge of the Greek philosophers and the wisdom of Eastern thinkers.

They did not understand when he elevated a life of love above the life of reason.

They shook their heads against him when he spoke of the Resurrection and Ascension of his Lord.

As the debate drew to its close the aged Xanthias, senior philosopher in the School and wisest scholar in Alexandria, said to Nicholas:

> 'Between what we call human intelligence and you call divine wisdom, Father Abbot;
> Between what we call human virtue and you call God's goodness;
> There is a chasm which we cannot bridge.
> Beyond what we have spoken;
> Beyond a knowledge bequeathed by the senses;
> There is a darkness which is everlastingly mysterious.'

Nicholas said quietly, almost as if speaking to himself:

'What you say is true, dear Xanthias. Our thoughts and His are far apart. We can reach but a little way to God. However He may stoop to us, talk with us and deal with us, if He so chooses. He may even become man to do this. Once there was a carpenter of Nazareth whose name was Joshua ben Joseph...,

***

Walking back with John, the Abbot observed:

'Is not Paul the beggar happier than all these wise? The path of doubt, strewn with painful rocks, runs a winding route through blowing sands. Those who use this path must travel in shadows. Let us keep in our prayers whom God has called to follow it.'

My steps have held fast to thy paths,
my feet have not slipped.
(Ps 17:5)

11
Reason

Where were you when I laid the
foundation of the earth?
Where is the way to the dwelling of light,
and where is the place of darkness...
that you may discern the paths to its home?
(Job 38:4,19,20)

The words from Job in that morning's reading surfaced to the mind of John the Dwarf. He was sitting beneath the afternoon clouds, on a low stool in the garden of Xanthias the Stoic. Puzzled by Nicholas' words during his visit to the School of Rhetoric, the philosopher had invited the Abbot to his home to speak privately with him. Gaunt and steeply stooped, his aged body had no hair and its skin fell like folds of cloth about him. But the outward demeanour of the simpleton disguised the jewelled mind of the city's most distinguished thinker. With his dearly loved grand-children, the twins Syncletica and Rufinus, he lived in a fine villa of rich brick and stone served by many slaves.

The Dwarf listened carefully as Nicholas invited Xanthias to set out his arguments. This he did with no hostility, but seriously and in truthful seeking.

Having pondered each argument, the Abbot took it and sculptured it further. Then he set it in a context which enriched, bequeathing to it an even more perfect shape. John thought:

Water from cupped hands, he pours into a silver
goblet.
He puts a pear into a bowl with apples and
pomegranates.
A peacock's egg is placed in the nest of the stork.

John also noticed the deep concentration with which Syncletica and Rufinus attended to Nicholas' words. The Abbot agreed with the philosopher that human reason was a mighty in-strument. Travelling further, he showed that it was also a mystery.

'The ear, though hearing the loveliest strains of the lyre, cannot explain its hearing. So reason, which seeks to explain all things, cannot explain itself to itself.'

The Abbot had also agreed that Ionian science and Ptolemaic astronomy were rich fruits of knowledge and testimonies to human intelligence. Then travelling further he showed that neither supported itself, but stood upon unknown foundations.

'Does a jar carry itself?
Will the javelin hurl itself?
May a crying babe rock herself to sleep?
Neither does knowledge rest on itself.
Beliefs and values, logic and opinions,
ever move beyond their own bounds to reside
in mystery.'

Xanthias listened thoughtfully while Nicholas suggested why reason would never give proof for the Holy One. He closed his argument quietly, simply saying:

'Clay does not fashion a potter
nor the hawk's flight a summer breeze.
Petals from a jasmine do not hang the sun in place,
nor may a carp unleash the surging deeps.
Neither will the net of reason take Him.

For it is He who makes the net.
From Him comes the light with which to discern
what reason traps.
He lies before all things and beyond all things,
yet still they bear the mark of His Making.'

Then looking round, as if a prayer was finished, he observed how intently each regarded him. Only John saw the flicker of a smile pass over his lips. His eyes danced as he said to Xanthias:

'The Great One holds reason as if it were a drop of
your rarest wine spilled on His beard.'

Xanthias piped with laughter and, taking Nicholas' arm to call a close to their talk, motioned the attendant to bring more wine. But Syncletica raised her hand slightly and asked leave to speak. Xanthias looked to Nicholas who nodded. How sweetly she speaks, thought John, as he watched her gracious figure rise. The afternoon breeze had played with her long, raven hair which was carelessly garlanded with crimson poppies and laurel leaves. Brushing it from her pale face and fixing her dark eyes on the Abbot, she put her points with crisp and penetrating simplicity beginning:

'Holy Father, your argument falters each time at
one gate.
Where knowledge fails there stands God.
At the bound of the known is His Shadow.
Is not the only name of your God, Ignorance?'

Nicholas, not noticing her outward beauty, took joy in the shining of her mind as she developed her argument. Truly Syncletica was a worthy grand-daughter for Xanthias. He replied using a parable:

'Now reason lives in a fine villa with many rooms.
The furniture in each room is a set of rules. One is
called chess, another farming, another warfare and

so on. Beyond this villa it is always night. Taking its lamp, reason may still explore outside and build further rooms. But always the darkness encompasses reason, never reason the darkness. So too finite reason is encompassed by the infinite darkness of God.'

Syncletica, unsatisfied, flashed directly back to Nicholas:

'Father Abbot, an argument from pictures carries the weakest force.'[26]

Nicholas shook his head. Speaking half to himself, he said:

'So again I fail. My pictures are not set within the tight house of reason to convince by logic. As enticements they seek first to lure you to its threshold, then to bring you outside its doors, Syncletica.

For is not reason too closely bounded?
What grammar marks the enchantment that
passes between lovers?
What logic contains the beauty of youth and the
wisdom of age?
What syntax gives answer to the riddle of death?

But poetry steps higher than reason. Only it can find the crack in reason's door. Yet I am not poet enough. I have not evoked for you He who dwells within and beyond all thinking.'

'But you have, Father Abbot,' said Rufinus moving quietly forward and kneeling before Nicholas for his blessing.

So it was that Rufinus began his quest for a wisdom beyond knowledge, a belief prior to thinking and a Love which guards all understanding.

12
Creation

Lift up your eyes on high and see:
who created these?
Have you not known? Have you not heard?
The Lord is...
the Creator of the ends of the earth.
(Is 40:26,28)

As he finished the afternoon meditation in the quiet garden of the monastery, shaded by a friendly cypress, John the Dwarf closed the Book of Isaiah. His mind turned again to Nicholas. The Abbot's sickness had visited him once more during the night. Beginning many years ago during his pilgrimage to Jerusalem, John noticed that it now fell upon him with a greater suddenness and was more stinging. Though he had humorously pretended to Bessarion that it was due to a surfeit of wine at the house of Xanthias, John knew that his Master had drunk no more than a few drops during all their stay there. The physician had been called and a potion mixed which now gave sleep to the Abbot's frail body.

John, who was now watching the porter explaining to Rufinus, had wanted to halt the lad's visit, but Nicholas would not have him delayed. He had drawn John close, saying:

'Be thou to him, my tongue.
Show thou to him, my love.
Open thou for him the gate.
He walks the Lord's Pathway.'

The Dwarf smiled in a detached way as he saw the

careless grace of this handsome twin of seventeen summers. Black curls toppled about a circlet of fresh orange blossoms as he trod the daisies down and came towards him. Some years had passed, thought John, since Nicholas had opened his own eyes to true beauty. His Master's words, given as they trod Scete's blazing desert, were carved into his mind:

'My son, all are apt to love, as falcons to fly or stars to shimmer.
Love's delight is His gift.
But only fools will stay at a walnut's case or the shell of the plover's egg.
Lissom limbs and ivory skin, honeyed breath and youth's keen eye, these hide a greater beauty which is His choicest gift.

What comeliness He bestows. Is not the loved one a temple for the Spirit and an heir of Heaven?
What radiance He bequeaths. Is she not Queen of Paradise, and he, Lord of Zion?
Made in His image, redeemed by Christ, beloved of angels,
Is not the smallest dwarf kin in beauty to the tallest prince?'

Such a sweet perception brought an acceptance which had opened John's eyes for tears.

***

The deep brown of Rufinus' shy eyes questioned John:

'Holy Brother, should I return after another sun…?'

But John waved his words aside and with a generous smile gave himself to the young man. He set out for Rufinus the teaching of the Nazarene. He told of his miracles, how he hung upon the tree, harrowed Hell and was hailed by angels on resurrection's fair morn. He showed the works and wonders of the disciples and the cost of this faith, for all gave their lives to it. They talked together for a long time and the young man's eyes burned. Then John, pausing to give himself space, said:

'Tell me of yourself, friend. How does Rufinus descry the world? What do you discover there? Speak, perhaps, of the Ineffable that I may take report back to the Abbot and cheer him.'

'The Ineffable is an inexhaustible melody, of which my life is but a single note.
When mathematics and philosophy have recited their most elegant visions, the prime letter of the first word in the book of this illimitable has not been drawn.
It inhabits herb and cherry's leaf, Aldebaran brightest of the Hyades[27] as well as the mighty Behemoth.[28] It is caught in a grain of sand.
That mystery which is manifest in rain and bread and earth, as well as the mind of His creatures, that is the Ineffable.

Is it not so, brother?'

The words were spoken as if with a strange music, addressing, it seemed to John, the horizon's very limit. The Dwarf realised that his question, intended simply to show friendship, moved through another gate. More deliberately this time he asked:

'Tell me of the Sublime, little brother.'

'It is an intimation that all things carry a reference beyond themselves.
It is what is spoken by the grasshopper and sung by the scorpion,
It is the speech of hyssop and rhetoric in the whisper of reeds.

Sensed in beauty, perceived in goodness and
embedded in truth, it moves outside all
knowledge, all words.
The child, astonished at the rainbow, wondering at
the ant, amazed at the strawberry's taste, lives in
the presence of the Sublime.

Is it not so, brother?'

The Dwarf nodded. They talked further and before he returned to his grandfather's house, he stayed for the evening prayers.

When I look at the heavens, the work of thy fingers,
the moon and the stars which thou hast
established;
what is man, that thou art mindful of him?...
Yet thou hast made him little less than God,
and dost crown him with glory and honour.
(Ps 8:3,4,5)

***

That evening, tending Nicholas, now awake and stronger, he spoke of Rufinus.

'Like his twin Syncletica, he inherits the mind of
Xanthias. He yet possesses one thing more than they.
Poesy inhabits his soul.
He sees the rising in the fallen;
He finds joy beneath tears;
He discovers the life given in death.'

Rejoicing, Nicholas said:

'His eyes have been lifted up on high.
He has seen Who created all these.'

13
Life

From heaven the Lord looked at the earth,
to hear the groans of the prisoners,
to set free those who were doomed to die.
(Ps 102:19,20)

A small side-door opened to let John and Nicholas into the dark passages of the prison in Alexandria. Holy Saturday had come to an early end, dimmed by a curtain of deep thunder clouds. At the monastery, the monks prepared to enter the long stillness of the vigil before resurrection's dawn. Bessarion, already in his travelling cloak, had told the Abbot and his disciple of a call to journey with all urgency to Cellia.[29]

'Will you go in my place to the Fortress and be a father to Markus?' he had asked.

So the two of them joined the slow traffic that trudged in and out of that shadowing place. John had heard the monks speak of Markus. A centurion with charge of the Governor's Guard, he had taken secret instruction in the faith. Betrayed by a jealous soldier, he had refused to burn incense to Caesar or worship his statue.

They entered the dismal cell which held him, isolated from all others, and told their errand. A sturdy man, tall and strong, whose beard and short cropped hair carried no grey, and whose eyes held no fear, he rejoiced at their coming and greeted them warmly. After prayers and psalms together, he ate and drank from the gifts the brothers had sent for him. Then he told Nicholas and John what Bessarion had feared most. It was what the brothers had prayed he might be saved from. At the Circus in the morning, held in honour of Caesar's birthday, he would be ground down by the beasts for the amusement of the mob. Roman justice saw him as a traitor.

Then Nicholas and he talked. Only half listening, the Dwarf's mind fled in sadness to the psalm said so recently, in remembrance of the carpenter from Nazareth.

> All who see me mock at me...
> Many bulls encompass me...
> They open wide their mouths at me...
> Save me from the mouth of the lion.
>
> (Ps 22:7,12,13,21)

He heard Nicholas explaining to Markus the Lord's descent into Hell.[30]

> 'He goes to that pit of blackest night,
> To them that crouch beneath death's wing.
> And first He sees old Adam bound in sin.
>
> 'Be awake, thou sleeping one. Rise from Death to
> Light.'
>
> And He takes him by the hand.
> He, Adam's God, who had become his Son;
> He, the Creator, who cast him in His Stamp;
> He, the Master, who became for him a Slave;
>
> 'Be awake, thou sleeping one. Rise from Death to
> Light.'
>
> He, who left the heavens, for the dust of earth,
> He, who took the spittle down his face,
> received the blows upon His cheeks,
> He, who slept upon a cross'd tree, embroidered in
> His red:
> Came to Death to bring him Life.

'Be awake, thou sleeping one. Rise from Death to
Light.

The cherubim have unbarred the gates of Paradise.
The throne is hewn and decked.
A banquet ready, everlasting chambers are
prepared.
The treasure chest being split, a Kingdom awaits
thee.
Awake! Arise!'

John listened and kept the prayers for each hour. He meditated on that God who died in the flesh that He might raise all from the flesh. He and the Abbot kept the fast and took only a little water, but both insisted that Markus eat. When Nicholas and the centurion had talked deep into the night, John saw his Master untie his pack and give a white robe to Markus. He put it on and in the guttering candles' light, with joy, he was baptised and received His Christ.

Then the good Abbot asked Markus to speak to him of death. The centurion, quietly, but without fear said:

'This is what the holy Bessarion has taught me and
I know it to be true from within my own spirit.

Death awaits as a strong steed, saddled and spurred,
to carry me to my Master's city.
She is a close friend who has crossed an ocean in
time to take me to her Lord, that I might delight
in Him.
She is a gate that opens onto fresh grass and meadow
flowers which lead to One who is Source for all
Loveliness.

At even the cranes fly homeward to their nests.
The bees return to hives filled with honey.
The chicks run to the mother's wing.
So does my soul yearn and seek for Him.'

'And what of Heaven?' asked Nicholas very gently, very quietly, but peering steadily into his eyes.

'It is that place, which being above all places is not a place, but the abode of His Love.
It is that music, which being beyond all music is not music, but the sound of His Voice.
It is that friendship, which being greater than all friends is not friendship, but union with Him.'

They put out the candles. They embraced. With the dawn was beginning all of the prison's business.

'Bessarion has taught him well,' said John.

The Abbot nodded.

***

In the monastery the great Easter Synaxis was celebrated. A soft spring breeze carried only the faintest shape of the crowd's roar from the Circus.

'My body given to be broken for you: Is the bread of Life.
My blood poured out for you: Is the wine of Love.'

Later, towards evening, the monks brought Markus' body, grievously torn, to their garden for its burial. Nicholas ordered it to be placed beneath a great plane tree by the south wall. Sprinkling it with white violets, he said:[31]

'He kissed us as he left us in the dark.
Now he is kissed as he enters the Light.'

Oh send out thy light and thy truth;
let them lead me,
let them bring me unto thy holy hill...
Then I will go to the altar of God,
to God my exceeding joy.

(Ps 43:3,4)

14
Suffering

Hear my prayer, O Lord...
For I am thy passing guest, a sojourner...
Look away from me, that I may know gladness,
before I depart and be no more!
(Ps 39:12-13)

The Easter season was drawing to its end when a letter came for Nicholas and John from the Fortress. In its infirmary the aged tribune Gaius Marius, who had subdued the Gallic tribes and stood against the Vandals,[32] was weak after a high fever. Yet he was resolute that the Abbot be sent for.

Attendants raised his taut and scarred body from a couch. Strength met strength as he and Nicholas looked into each other's eyes. He gave a stiff and formal greeting.

'I saw Markus die,' he said abruptly. 'As a centurion he was permitted a short sword. Most fall upon it immediately. He did not. Instead he gave protection to others, slaves, prisoners and their families. With great skill he killed two of the fiercest beasts until, slipping in a spurt of blood, he fell to other gaping jaws.'

***

While the tribune spoke of the Circus, John sat apart against a wall of the infirmary and said the prayers and readings for that hour.

I will fall upon them like a bear robbed of her cubs,
I will tear open their breast,
and there I will devour them like a lion.

(Hosea 13:8)

***

'Before he entered the arena Markus told me of your visit during the night and asked me to speak with you of his end. This duty is now done. A fool has met his death.'

There was, thought John, both anger and sadness in Gaius' voice.

'A fool?' said Nicholas, seeing the part set for him.

'As the leopard's leap breaks the gazelle,
And the falcon's dive tears the dove,
So does the suffering our soldiers see
Shatter the superstition of God,' answered Gaius fiercely.

'But may not God and suffering co-exist?' said Nicholas. 'When evil befalls, may it not be a deserved punishment for wrongdoing? Will not the Prefect imprison thieves?'

'Such a thought is too small. How will it house infants disembowelled for sport in the camps of the Goths?[33] If this is punishment for guilt, your defence is worse than my disbelief', replied Gaius dismissively.

Nicholas thought a while. 'Let us set a larger thought. Suffering that ends in death, is it not the smaller part of a greater good? Ants that fall into the Nile feed the fish on which my lord and his guests feast?'

'Such a thought is twisted', Gaius said curtly. 'How will it hold ten thousand Roman soldiers, forced to their deaths over the great cliffs of Volsco after the battle of Atria? When the panorama renders suffering invisible, justice and humanity are betrayed.'

***

John crept into the small garden at the back of the Fortress and in deep stillness read the lessons for that hour.

> The Lord has destroyed without mercy
> all the habitations of Jacob...
> Infants and babes faint in the streets of the city.
> They cry to their mothers, 'Where is bread and wine?'
> as they faint...
> as their life is poured out on their mothers' bosom.
> (Lamentations 2:2,11,12)

***

Again Nicholas pondered. 'Let us shape a different thought. When suffering is overcome, is there not a deepening of the human spirit? The pain of hard training enables a wrestler to win his bout? The misery of a child, beaten to learn his letters, turns to joy once he travels with Homer?' [34]

Gaius looked fiercely at the Abbot. 'This thought accepts a small truth but is defeated by a larger. Can it contain those Roman virgins so cruelly ravaged by the Scythians?[35] Suffering ennobles a few but destroys many.'

'Then let us draw a thought that includes eternity. Does immortality stand as an assurance that suffering will not reign forever?' said Nicholas rather deliberately.

'Will you thus sweep away the cruelties and horrors of all ages? This thought confirms that suffering has no meaning in history.' Gaius Marius shook in anger. Tears stood in his eyes.

Nicholas moved closer. 'Before he died Markus told me that he was your son. He spoke lovingly of you, even at our leaving.'

Gaius gave a sharp and joyless laugh. 'Will a Christian wizard try to comfort a dying Stoic?'[36]

'No', said the Abbot, 'but now I will give you my answer to your question. Thus far we have been as little twin brothers playing in a strange garden. We have opened four doors in its wall but found no paths. I, too, know my arguments fail. But change the picture. Go back in time to a shared womb. How could we know our mother in whom we live? How might I speak to you of her? How would you hear me? Clearly she is, to us, unknowable, though she sustains us and we live in her love.

So is God Unknowable. Suffering is a mystery that lies within this Unknowing. But remember, it is a tunic that He also wears. Once He donned it for death on a black tree. Such suffering has no warrant outside His Freedom to be Himself. He may choose His own tunic. There can be then no theory to explain this, only love surrendering itself to Him as He is.'

'So one mystery explains another? You compound ignorance.'

'The person unable to love the Incomprehensible must despair, for He embeds all meaning.'

'Again we come to the gulf between the Stoa and Zion',[37] he gasped and fell back on his couch, waving them away.

***

Walking back to the monastery John the Dwarf and his Master paused to say their psalms.

> Though the fig tree do not blossom,
>   nor the fruit be on the vines,
> the produce of the olive fail
>   and the fields yield no food…
>   and there be no herd in the stalls,
> yet I will rejoice in the Lord.
>
> (Habakkuk 3:17-18)

15
Child

The dense sand storms lasted for three weeks and delayed the messenger. It was just after Pentecost[38] when Nicholas received Bessarion's letter. Before he and John could join him in Cellia, the baby was born.

'This has brought scandal to the brothers in the monastery', said Bessarion with a worried frown. The Abbot and John the Dwarf had arrived in time for the night prayer. Following it Bessarion took them quickly to his room. While they ate the figs and cheese prepared for their supper, he explained what had occurred.

'It concerns Sarah and Pinufius. She is daughter to Arminion, one of our farmers. Each week she brought fresh vegetables to the monastery. Brother Pinufius, who was assigned to the accounts, gave payment. Each week last year in secret, their love sprang higher. At St Michael's Mass he took full knowledge of her, though with her sincere agreement. She is now seventeen summers and he but twenty. The infant is six days old.'

***

John's head echoed with the psalm which they had said at their night prayer.

> Your robes are all fragrant with
> myrrh and aloes and cassia...
> at your right hand stands the queen in gold of
> Ophir.[39]

The princess is decked... with gold-woven robes;
in many-coloured robes she is led to the king.
(Ps 45:8,9,13,14)

***

'When it was known she was with child, Arminion cast her away. She came here. The brothers confined each to separate, locked cells, giving them meagre fare. They intended this imprisonment as a period for repentance. As each of their lives slowly faded, though from love or the brothers' punishment who can know, I was sent for. This monastery is part of our greater charge from Alexandria.'

'You nourished and set them free?' asked Nicholas.

'Indeed', said Bessarion, 'though she was so weak that we feared for the child. Yet both are still with us.'

'Will you release him from his vows?' queried the Abbot.

'That is done already. But as you know, the Rule forbids women and children. Here neither may stay. Even now the scandal grows daily. Yet these young ones have no kinsmen to support them. Whither can they go?'

John the Dwarf came close to Nicholas and whispered in his ear. The Abbot smiled.

'Of course, they must go to Alexandria, to Pambo the Tall, and cast accounts for the seller of that city's best wines. I will write a letter. In the morning let us speak with them.'

***

The sun was still low, cool enough for the little group to sit under the orange trees by the Chapel wall.[40] Arrangements were made, thanks given. Sarah and Pinufius, shining with the simplicity of love, ate pomegranates.[41] Unconcerned, Ichabod[42] slept on a lamb's fleece in a crib of newly woven twigs and grasses. The brother spoke for both of them. His dark eyes flashed with intelligence in the telling of joy at their imprisonment.

As a bee chooses not a crocus or a marigold
  But takes honey equally;
As a white stork prefers not an eel to a carp
  But feeds equally;
So we two found, in what was given and what was
  withheld;
In what was said and unsaid; in the done and not
  done;
In heat as in cold; in light as in shadow;
In lack as in plenty; in sameness as in difference;
  An equal love from God.

A coming creation, a likeness of His Image,
Ichabod, in sweet juice of our love,
Turned for us, stale water to spiced wine,
Sour bread to almonds, dry roots to mulberries.
He moved two bare cells to a Garden of Paradise,
  excelling
All that Jannes and Jambres[43] conjured from thin
  desert air.

'And', said Nicholas softly, 'what of Ichabod for himself?'

Sarah smiled shyly. Pinufius touched her honeyed cheek and gently stroked her hair, as she looked at him. There was strength and goodness behind her laughter. Then she said, 'That was our question for you. Instruct us before we go, Holy Father.'

Nicholas looked far into the sky, then very intently at them.

'My children, this tiny infant is for God, for all and for you.

Ichabod is a sign for God.
Like a rose of Sharon, he points to Beauty beyond all blossoms.
He is a reference for One standing beyond all reference.
He is an expression of a Mystery set outside all expression.
Like a Tamarisk bush in the desert, unseen or seen, he sings the Creator's love.
As a kingfisher waits for clear water to see his catch, so in this child's patience, God waits to seize His prey of love.

Ichabod is for us all. Men and women will find God in him.
Within his fleeting joys, there will be Joy unfading.
Through his silences, Eternity will echo in human hearts.
In his pain, there will be awe at the Mystery of death.

And Ichabod is for you.
He gives a remembrance of the scent of summer gar lands, which crowned your loving with a gift of His Image.
He ties himself to you, for his growing is your growing, his wisdom brings your wisdom.
He asks to be set free, for the journey he makes is not your journey, and is made at a time that is not your time, and is set among companions who are not of your choosing.'

***

Within a month a caravan came through Cellia set for Alexandria. Watching the three join the traders and then meander towards an empty horizon, John the Dwarf murmured, 'The infant was not well named Ichabod. Has Pinufius the Hebrew tongue? Knew he not its meaning: "The glory has gone"?'

'It was the brothers' choice', Bessarion quickly replied. 'They hoped the infant would remind Pinufius of his broken vocation and the cost of his lust.'

'They were too strict', sighed Nicholas. 'Could they not see that the lad was not destined for the desert life?' Where they said lust, did none suspect love? They have, perhaps, lived too close to their own temptations.

In their hearts, Sarah and Pinufius know that little Ichabod has another name – "Immanuel, God with us".'[44]

16
Dreams

'How are you fallen from heaven,
O Day Star, son of the Dawn!...
You said in your heart,
'I will ascend to heaven; above the stars of God...
I will make myself like the Most High.'
But you are brought down... to the depths of the Pit...
maggots are the bed beneath you,
and worms are your covering.

(Isaiah 14:12-15.11)

A low mist hung over the desert wastes as Abbot Nicholas and John the Dwarf set out from Cellia for their own place of solitude in Nitria. After several miles, as they paused to say the psalms of the hour, the disciple noticed that his Master's sickness was set to return.

The aged Macarius, slight in build and frail from the rigour of his ascetic practices, gave them refreshment and shelter in the small guest chamber attached to his cell. Gentle and sweet-tempered, his hospitality was simple but courteous.

The brethren in that place held him in awe for the strictness of his life. It was rumoured that he had begun the desert way by standing in prayer for six months. Some claimed that through all his years he slept but one hour each night. Others said that, besides canonical fasts on Wednesdays and Fridays, for three further days each week, he took only green herbs and water. It was even whispered that the Archangel brought him food from Heaven. Many were certain that he performed wonders.

***

While the Abbot lay in a deep sleep, John and Marcarius said their prayers together.

> The tongue is a fire...
> How great a forest is set ablaze by a small fire!
> The tongue is... set on fire by Hell.
>
> (James 3:5-6)

***

For three days Nicholas rested. During that time John noticed that when he and Macarius spoke, their host was anxious to narrate the trials and torments which his own Master, the holy Piammonas, had endured many years before.

> 'The Evil One visited my Master under cunning guises and with many temptations. Once, God left him in dryness of spirit for three years. Then in the first week of the season of Lent when he lived only on thin herb soup, there visited him late one night a stranger wrapped in a richly woven cloak of purple.
>
> 'He who is the High One has sent me. He has bidden me bring:
>
> A goblet, kissed to its lip with honey and fruits' juice;
> A dish, bathing meats of lamb and kid with rarest herbs;
> A bowl, whose sides embrace fine figs and sweet grapes.
>
> He says, "Partake, be at your ease, your trials are done." '

At this the blessed Piammonas hurled a flaming torch at the apparition, shouting these words:

> "Truly thou art named the Liar.[45] The richest food is the food of fasting: that which most sustains is the spiritual meat which nourishes the soul."

In the second week of the season of Lent again at night, as he knelt in prayer, there came to his cell the King of Babylon with the princes and ladies, the servants and entertainers of all his court. They feasted, drank and indulged in unseemly behaviour, ever beckoning Piammonas to join them in lewd revels. Finally the King took him to a secret chamber. It was hung with bright tapestries and around it were couches of costly silken cushions. Upon them lay the King's most desirable concubines. Each was naked; each wondrously perfumed; each held her arms to receive my Master.

The holy Piammonas spoke these words as slowly he knelt again to pray in the dust of the cell floor:

> "Truly thou art called the Tempter. Think not to confuse me betwixt lust and love. The one subjects creatures to the creaturely. The other frees them to journey to that Sun whose dazzling is union with Him."

In the third week of the season of Lent in the stillness of the blackest of desert nights, a messenger came to the door of his cell. He gave him news of an inheritance which brought him riches and lands beyond any imagining.

> "Your abode will be the towers of golden palaces set in parks and mountains. Your tunics will be of fine silks, your cloaks of fur. Princesses shall serve you and warriors await your bidding. Many peoples will be subject to your rule. Take up your destiny."

Blessed Piammonas took his staff to beat the messenger saying:

> "Truly thou art called the Prince of This World for thou hast no claim on the next. Indeed I am an heir, but of that Kingdom which esteems poverty, hon-

ours sacrifice and elevates loving-kindness and suffering over power and strength."'

***

As Nicholas and John continued their journey, the Dwarf spoke of Macarius and the trials of Piammonas. The Abbot listened thoughtfully. Finally, after walking for some time in silence he said:

'The desert cell is Hell's cockpit no less than a royal palace or the traders' bazaar, a maiden's thighs or the scholar's desk.

But what is played out there takes its costume from the hidden thought of each actor.
Shape and symbol are invested with power from conjoined dread and desire, both drawn from a soul's deepest wells.

Does water with a place below in which to flow, rise?
Will the moth's flight circle away from a burning candle?
Can a suckling babe turn its head from the paps which feed?
So must the Evil One use what each presents to him.
And in the desert, fasting and celibacy, poverty and weakness are paths used by him with sly cunning.[46]

As a lover will stand in the place of his beloved;
As the valley echoes a song chanted on the mountain's side;
As a child's shadow cannot be split and separated from her;
So Macarius finds Piammonas twin to his own dreams.'

John was silent for some time. Then he asked: 'Those brethren who are untutored have hitched to the good Macarius wondrous spiritual feats. Is this to sustain their own faith?'

Nicholas said: 'As the brothers allow logic to discriminate between thoughts, so must they allow love to discriminate between miracles, between dreams, between visions, and between hopes. For it is only love that sustains and leads faith.'

17
Prayer

When they arrived at their cells in the Nitrian wastes Abbot Nicholas and John the Dwarf found them cleaned, the courtyard swept and food prepared. Salt-bread, cheese and a jug of fresh water awaited them. The brothers had learned from Christian travellers in a merchants' caravan that Master and disciple approached. So they chose Peter, the newest deacon, to prepare their welcome.

He embraced them with sincere love and giving a cheerful, open smile, took off their dusty cloaks and washed their feet. Then together they said the psalms of the hour.

> Love the Lord, all you his saints!
> The Lord preserves the faithful…
> Be strong, and let your heart take courage,
> all you who wait for the Lord!
>
> (Ps 31:23-24)

While they ate, the youngster passed to them news of the other brothers. Abbot Copres and Didymus the Holy had both died; the first of great age and the second of desert fever. Brothers Daniel and Anoub had been forced, against their will, back to Alexandria to serve as soldiers.[47] Those who had joined the brothers recently spoke of a persecution in that city, of riots and the destruction by fire of Apollo's Temple.

Peter the Deacon remained to serve them for two days. The third day was a Sabbath so they set out together to join their brothers in the celebration of the Synaxis. At its end there were joyous greetings for John and Nicholas and personal stories to share with many of their friends.

'Holy Father,' whispered John to Nicholas with mirth in his voice, 'does a king have more than one chamberlain? May a merchant ride two donkeys at the same time?'

'I have noticed him too', said Nicholas, his eyes twinkling.

He turned and beckoned to Peter. Strangely the deacon, whose duties were now completed, yet continued with them.

'How may my friend and I thank you for your service to us?' asked the Abbot. Then quickly he placed his arm gently on the boy's shoulder as he saw tears run down the cheeks of the bowed head.

'Holy Father, teach me the meaning of prayer. I know it not.'

***

They sat in Peter's tiny cell. The Abbot listened for a long time until the rush of words came to its end. Then he spoke quietly and simply as to one deeply loved.

> 'Reflect, my son. Do you walk too quickly for God?
> Hear that song which the Lord sings with your life.
> Recall that:
>
> There is one time for the lattices of heaven[48] to give dew,
> And another for the sun to fire the sands.
> There is one time for children to play with coloured toys,
> And another when they rest upon their pallets.
> There is a time when life blooms and youth is all,
> And another when white hairs close life's door.'

Peter said: 'Pray for me, Father, that I may be more measured.'

'Reflect again my son. Do you climb too high for God?
Is the cup which a thirsty potter makes for himself as the goblet from which the Lord of the Farthest Isles drinks?
Recall that a solitary:
Seeks not the voice of God, but hears it in cracking ice, blowing reeds and brethren's laughter.
Seeks not the gifts of God, but finds them in new bread, the darkness of dawn and brethren's love.
Seeks not the vision of God, but 'spies His Print on bee's wing, fishes' fin and brother's heart.'

Peter said: 'Pray for me, Father, that I may be more lowly.'

'Reflect again, my son. Do you ask too much of God?
What has a dung collector to offer his son? Nought but love.
Know that:
When His prize is downfalling, you may find a rising.
When His favour is silence, you may catch a melody.
When His blessing is suffering, you may sense deep peace.
For Him Betwixt quiet and tumult, there is parity.
For Him betwixt strength and weakness, there is parity.
For Him betwixt an instant and an age, there is parity.
So:
The heart of darkness is new light.
The heart of despair is fresh hope.
The heart of death is eternal life.

Only those who have nothing can accept
everything.

Peter said: 'Pray for me, Father, that I may be more simple.'

***

After the long silence that followed this conversation, John spoke quietly to Nicholas who looked saddened but then nodded gently. So it happened that Peter the Deacon was placed with a Greek slave, the aged Hyllas. Though newly settled in Nitria from a cell in Scete, already the brothers valued his wisdom and holiness. From him Peter would receive support and guidance in his path to God.

***

As they walked back to their own cell John said to Nicholas: 'Does Peter see yet his life is a prayer uttered by God?'

'Not yet, though Hyllas will teach him
to cease from useless struggle,
to endow the form of prayer with the substance of love.
He will help him
to be himself in adoration,
to be genuine in thanksgiving and
to be honest in confession.
He will shape in him that wisdom which gives:
Ears to hear the movement of the Father in His Universe,
Eyes to see the Creator's mark in all that is made,
Wit to find in the Psalms the very habitation of Christ.[49]

But let us pray not only for Peter, but also for our brother Simon the Deacon, now entered into that Holy City above.'

> Oh send out thy light and thy truth;
>   let them lead me,
> let them bring me to thy holy hill
>   and to thy dwelling!
>
> (Ps 43:3)

18
Justice

And Mary said,
'My soul magnifies the Lord,
And my spirit rejoices in God my Saviour...
For he who is mighty has done great
things for me...'

(Luke 1:46-47.49)

As the time for the remembrance of the Nativity of the Christ Child drew near, the Lady Helena again visited Nicholas and John. She was a wealthy widow of a questioning faith and a wide generosity to the poor in Alexandria. Each year at this season she brought gifts for the Abbot and his disciple.

His teacher of many years before, Democritus the Greek, tutor to the sons of the Imperial Court at Rome, had instilled a high regard for ancient literature in Nicholas. And the only gifts he would receive from the Lady Helena were written scrolls. At each coming, playfully, she chided him for the wealth of knowledge in his book chest. Each time he gave the same robust answer:

> 'So great is the Wisdom of the Mighty One that human knowledge and ignorance are alike to Him.'

She and her servants lodged in the guest cells for two nights. During the day she prayed the Hours with her hosts, read the Scriptures and meditated in private. The evening before her departure, following prayers and a sparse meal, she said to Nicholas and John: 'I have a story which requires judgement. Will you hear it?' They agreed. With a disturbed look set in her fine grey eyes she began.

***

'My terrible tale is about Ithamar, an Israelite of ancient lineage.[50] Of the priestly class, a Levite, he came from the hill country of Ephraim. During that time when Israel had no king, he travelled to Bethlehem to secure a concubine. There Silshar, son of Ner, agreed a sum with him for his youngest daughter, the beautiful Mischael. Looking upon her he loved her and took her to his home in Ephraim. But there his behaviour disturbed her and she fled, returning to her father.

After a year and four months Ithamar was moved to reclaim his concubine. Taking with him a servant and two asses, he set out for Bethlehem, determined to speak kindly and win her again. Silshar greeted him with the most lavish hospitality. A kid was killed and the strongest wine was set forth. For four days they feasted together with great merriment. It was agreed that Mischael should return with him. But all of Ithamar's converse was with his father-in-law. He did not speak to the maiden. On the afternoon of the fifth day the Levite, his servant and his concubine set out from Bethlehem to Ephraim.

The day lengthened and they passed the city of Jebus.[51] But its inhabitants were not of the tribes of Israel, so Ithamar did not rest there. When they arrived at Gibeah, a city of the tribe of Benjamin, the sun had set. They went inside the city gates and, as was the custom, sat in the market square. But none among the inhabitants offered them lodging. It was not until late evening that they found hospitality with an elderly man called Thamah. Though he sojourned in Gibeah he was not a Benjaminite, but like Ithamar came from the hill country of Ephraim.

As the little group ate and drank in his house, there was a great noise outside and a battering of the door. Men of the city demanded that Thamah should give them his male guest, that they might do with him those things which are not to be spoken of among us. At this the terrified Ithamar seized Mischael and pushed her outside for the crowd.

> And they raped her and abused her
> throughout the night, and at dawn
> they let her go.[52]

In this first light she struggled to the porch of Thamah's house and lay in great suffering, awaiting her journey to death. At full light Ithamar opened the door to set out for his own country and found her. Her hand stretched towards him across the threshold. 'Come,' he said, 'arise. We must start back now.' But she could not speak to him. So he placed her on one of the asses and they came back to Ephraim.

Once in his own dwelling, taking a knife, he seized her and cut her up, limb by limb, into twelve parts. To each of twelve servants he gave a part. 'Go to all of the tribes of Israel and say: Has there been such a deed as this?' And it was done. Each tribe, seeing her, said: 'Such a thing has not occurred since Israel came out of Egypt, even to this day.' And the tribes of Israel took vengeance on the Benjaminites killing twenty and five thousand of them.'

***

The Lady Helena in the merest whisper said: 'Make a judgement, John the Dwarf. Was Ithamar justified in his actions?'

John replied seriously: 'Was it not a custom of the ancients that concubines were chattels of their lord? So then his deeds were just. A man may only be judged with justice from within his own times.'

The Lady Helena looked at Nicholas. He said thoughtfully:

> 'Holy Paul the Apostle speaks of a law that is written on human hearts.[53] And Our Lord Himself[54] asks the crowd, "Why do you not judge for yourselves what is right?" What can we understand such words to mean?
>
> Whether the kite nests in Cush or in Erech,[55]
> does the keenness of its vision change?
> Whether the warrior fights in No-Amon[56] or
> Babylon does his skill vary?
> Whether a royal princess is in Bozrah or
> Heshbon,[57] does her beauty decline?
>
> So through all time, at every place, within all
> peoples, is heard the whisper of God.
> Those who chose to take others for their own fell
> purposes have stopped their ears to it.
> Let us remember them and their victims in our
> prayers, for they are very many.'

He looked at the Lady Helena and said: 'You have two answers, Lady, which do you choose? Justice or Love?'

***

> Then Herod... was in a furious rage, and he sent and killed all the male children in Bethlehem, and in all that region, who were two years old or under...
>
> A voice was heard in Ramah, wailing and loud lamentation, Rachel weeping for her children; she refused to be consoled because they were no more.
>
> (Matthew 2:16,18)

19
Jew

In Judah God is known,
his name is great in Israel.
His abode has been established in Salem,
his dwelling place in Zion.

(Ps 76:1,2)

At first they thought that he was dead. The caravan stopped but briefly to leave the Jew with Abbot Nicholas and John the Dwarf.

> 'He stepped into a nest of scorpions. Now their poison does its work. We travel quickly and cannot comfort him. Let him die in peace or lodge until we return. You will be well-paid.'

So the Steward sought hospitality and healing for Jeshua the Scribe.[58] He beckoned three slaves. Two carried the sick man, obviously in a high fever, to the guest chamber. The other brought a small chest and placed it by the sleeping mat.

***

While John washed Jeshua's body, Nicholas prepared a compress of figs for the foot and a drink of vinegar and desert herbs.

The fever remained for ten days and nights during which time the Scribe drifted in and out of consciousness. On the morning of the eleventh day he revived. Sitting up a little he firmly refused Nicholas' medicine.

‘It tastes like wine from the vine of Sodom,’[59] he whispered.

‘… and… the fields of Gomorrah; their grapes… are bitter; their wine is the poison of serpents…’ said Nicholas finishing the scripture for him, before bursting into friendly laughter.

***

As Jeshua regained his health, he proved a cheerful and considerate guest. A middle-aged, slightly built man, whose beard was already flecked with grey, he was from a noble family in Jerusalem. He had journeyed to Egypt to claim an inheritance. Now he waited with patience the return of the caravan. As the days went by his friendship with his hosts quickly grew. Talking quietly to John one hot afternoon, in the shade of the courtyard wall, he said: ‘May I ask you three questions?’ John smiled, guessing what was to follow.

‘The first is this. When sick did I drink wine[60] or eat what crawls or creeps?[61] Did I partake of cheese and fowl together?’[62]

‘My friend, when the Abbot knew you were of the ancient race he took care to provide only what your Law allows. The wine you drank was not offered to idols. Of what crawls, you ate locusts. But that is permitted. Cheese too you ate. Yet not with fowl – is this a king’s house that we eat flesh daily?’ John laughed at the idea. Jeshua smiled and continued:

‘The second is this. Is my guest chamber a place where any other seeking your consolation has died?’[64]

‘My friend, none has given up life here. Though for some days we feared for you! You are not made impure by a shadow from any sad corpse’, said the Dwarf. Jeshua went on:

'The third is this. In washing and binding me each day, did you observe any bodily discharge?[64]

'None', said Nicholas, who had arrived unnoticed. 'Do not fear, you are not unclean. Though our knowledge is small and provisions few, we met your Codes where we could. Though of course,' he added his eyes dancing, 'you eat, drink, rest and gain strength for life, in the cells of two desperate Gentiles.'

***

Brightness returned to Jeshua's face. There was relief that no impurity had been committed and lightness at Nicholas' gentle humour. Then he said quietly:

'You have preserved my life for me. In doing that you have obeyed the heart of Israel's Law, for it gives life. When flesh and blood are threatened, lesser precepts sleep. The School to which I am bound argues that men should live through the law, not find death in it.'[65]

Nicholas said: 'Our Law gives life too. In his care that your life might return, John showed his love. That is the Master's Way which is our Law. Among us it is called the Law of Love.'

'Perhaps', said Jeshua very slowly, 'our two ways are like twin rivers which followed the same course for a great while before separating. Will they meet again?'

Nicholas pondered for some time, then said:

> 'May not two wrestlers train for the same contest with differing teachers, diet and exercise, yet both fight well?
>
> Each follows the advice of his tutor.
> Each eats what is given for power.
> Each performs the set movements.

But why? To what end? Is it that each may know:
The gladness of strength and delight in skill,
The excitement of combat and the joy of victory?
Yes, but more. What each becomes bathes all his life.
Yet, grey with time, as each road closes, may they not meet, embrace, laugh and weep a little at youth's shadows?'

Thus the practices of religion prepare for what stretches far beyond them.

The Law is a friend, drawing to His Very Presence.
Through its observance spirit rejoices with Spirit.
Its outwardly shape gives shelter to Truth.
So purity in body sings a perfection of heart.
So discipline reveals Love.

There will be a day my friend when, in the stillness of contemplation, He will give us love enough to call each other first neighbour, then brother. Finally we shall see not Jeshua, not Nicholas – only Him. We will meet again.'

***

As he left to join the caravan, Jeshua opened his small chest and gravely presented to Master and disciple two prayer shawls.

Watching him depart John said: 'So goes the Hebrew Jeshua. Does he know the Greek form of his name?'

'Yes, I think he knows', said Nicholas, 'that it is Jesus.'

20
Mystic

O that I had wings like a dove!
I would fly away and be at rest;
yea, I would wander afar,
I would lodge in the wilderness.

(Ps 55:6-7)

John saw from the camel's dung beyond the courtyard that Nicholas had received a visitor. Three weeks earlier the Abbot's beloved disciple had taken messages to Abbot Bessarion in Alexandria. Returning now he was greeted with gentleness by his Master. While he ate salt bread, figs and cheese Nicholas talked.

'You have gifts from the aged Abbot Silvanus, of which he has told me. For six days he lodged here and spoke warmly of you. Yesterday he left. He seeks that greater silence which solitary living in the western deserts will give.'

The sun rose a second time that day for John at the name Silvanus. In an instant, many years fell away and the Dwarf saw himself once more a child. Terrified, the naked boy was paraded at the slave market in Corinth for a whole day. All who looked were ribald. None offered for him. At even for a cheap skin of sour wine, he was given to Lychas, Master of Freaks. On each market day, his procession of human monsters and imbeciles entertained those who traded with songs and tumbles. John learned to juggle and amused the crowds with his clumsy somersaults. But Lychas always demanded more and taught him lascivious movements and immodest dancing to the music of pipes and tambourine. Each part of his painful and mis-shapen body was cruelly exposed to the gloating and derision of others.

In his fifteenth year he contracted a high fever. But Lychas refused him care and medicine. Now a useless and broken tool, he was left to die in the rot and stench of the market place. From there old Silvanus, teller of stories and deacon of the Church of Christ in Corinth, rescued him and nursed him to health again.

***

Each gift was wrapped separately. The first, fitting neatly into the palm of John's hand, was a desert stone. Beautifully polished, it had a hole sculptured through its centre. The Dwarf smiled and said:

> 'With this I am to remember his story of the ants who lived in a small garden. It was surrounded by a high stone wall. The ants worked and played, built and farmed, made war and peace, lived and died, all in that little space. Only one ant did not share in the activities of the others. So they asked him:
>
> "Why do you sit and look at the wall all day?" He answered: "So that I can understand how a stone may be pierced. Then I shall crawl through it to what lies beyond." '

Nicholas nodded:

> 'Does a beggar lost in a wood not seek a track to its edge?
> Will a soldier wounded in battle not cry for healing?
> Can an inn-keeper pay no heed to the knocking on his doors?
> So all are called to begin the journey set for them,
> And to see that it is a journey without distance.

Silvanus bids you continue for ever your pursuit of Christ, the Beloved One who draws you to His side.'

***

The second gift was a beautiful wooden carving of a small frog. John laughed and glancing at his Master, said:

'With this I am to remember the story of those frogs who were theologians. They were very learned but they could not agree among themselves about God. They felt that his supernatural shape was certainly frog-like. Yet some held that He had two heads and four legs, others that He had three eyes and two tongues and a few that His heads, legs, eyes and tongues were countless!'

Nicholas grinned:

'Can he who drinks new wine of roses, shape
words to tell it?
Can lovers' delights be set within the frame of
language?
How may a mother utter her joy that her child grows
in grace?
So what is explained is the least part of meaning.
Similitudes point only to a silence which
expresses All.

Silvanus bids you to explore the darkness of solitude until you find what mind cannot translate and tongue may not say.'

***

The third gift was a small whistle, skilfully made in silver, With good cheer in his voice, John said:

‘With this I am to remember the story of the two birds. One, who had lived in the same wood all of her life, spoke to another who travelled through it. Said the first: “I have been searching for Ruach[66] for many years. It is said that she will sustain and bring joy. But I have not found her. She is not in this wood. Have you seen her?” Said the second who was wiser: “Already you know her. You meet her each day. She does sustain and bring you joy. Without her you would not fly. On her breath she brings you food. She cools you when you are hot. She sings her music to you at all times. Your friend Ruach is the wind!”’

Nicholas spoke quietly:

‘Silvanus bids you search for the shadow of the Lord Christ. Does it not stretch through our daily psalms?

King David shows His birth at the House of Bread:[67]
“From the womb[68] of the morning like dew your
youth will come to you.”
He sees Him drain the chalice of His passion: “He
will drink from the brook by the way.”
It is given to him to know His Ascension and
Glorification: “Sit at my right hand.”

So His shadow falls across even such lives as ours.’

John carefully placed Silvanus’ gifts on a ledge saying: ‘More than all else I will remember his words as he took me, dying from the market in Corinth, to his own home. He said:

“Know that the One who flings the stars to heaven,
and pours out the great seas;
Know that He who paints the beauty of the peacock,
and gives the lark her song;
Know that it is He, who in His love, created thee.”’

21
Shekhinah

My heart overflows with a goodly theme;
I address my verses to the king...
You are the fairest of the sons of men;
grace is poured upon your lips.

(Ps 45:1,2)

As soon as he had finished the afternoon psalms, anxiously John returned to the small courtyard. Standing in the gateway he scanned the horizon for his Master. Nicholas was two days late returning from Pispir. He had determined to travel on his own to spend a little time with Hierax, Spyridon and young Xoius, whose souls he now guarded. 'For', he had said to John, with eyes full of mirth, 'on a long journey alone, the Mighty One will have the time that He needs to reprove me fully.'

As John was about to light the lamps in the cells, he saw the merest speck on the darkening horizon. Quickly, he set out to meet the Abbot. It was clear to him that Nicholas' fever had returned during his journey back. For five days he tended and watched over him, once more noticing how deeply, in recent months, the illness clawed at his life. As so often now, he said the psalms for them both.

Thy arrows have sunk into me,
and thy hand has come down on me...
I am utterly bowed down...
I am... spent and crushed.

(Ps 38:2,6,8)

***

'I took refuge at a small oasis for some time. In my resting strange things came to me. On the first day I saw at the edge of the oasis a clearing empty but for one very old tree. A child came and knelt beside it.

"What are you doing?" I asked. Very softly answer was given.

"I am listening to the tree."

"What does it say to you?"

The reply was the merest whisper. "That it has no purpose but to be itself."

Astonished I said: "How can a tree have such understanding?"

"In its silence."

Though whether this answer came from the lips of the child, the wind of the desert, the leaves of the tree – or my own heart – I cannot tell. Then I looked into the eyes of the child. Within them was that light which shone in the eyes of Moses as he saw the Burning Bush.'[69]

***

'In the night-time I was awakened by the cry of a soldier. He stood in a rocky valley and I watched as he fought a monstrous snake. Bravely he cut its head off. Then strangely it became a roaring lion. Piercing its heart it changed to become a beautiful maiden, full of beckoning and sweet speech. As he sunk his sword in her, she fell to the ground and took on her true form. She was the hideous offspring of Beelzebub.[70] Amazed I asked what he did.

He said:

> "I return the wisdom which the snake would
> give me.

It is empty and may not aspire to the Holy One.
I return the strength which the lion would bestow.
It is hollow and cannot capture or hold the Great One.
I return the sweetness of spiritual allurements.
They are trifles which bind and blind to His Purity."

Then I look into the eyes of the soldier. Within them was that light which shone in the eyes of Abraham on a mountain in the land of Moriah[71] as he raised the knife to Isaac.'

***

'On the second day it was as if I walked through the great market in Alexandria. Amidst the din of all of those selling fine linen, perfumes and sweet-meats sat a man at an empty stall. Dressed in rags, he did not shout for trade. All ignored him. I said: "What do you sell?"

"Nothing", he replied.

"How may I buy nothing?" I asked.

He answered:

"Give me all your possessions and I will give you nothing.
Give me all your learning and I will give you nothing.
Give me all your delights and I will give you nothing.

When you are detached from earthly things;
When you are empty of spiritual treasures;
When you are in poverty of spirit;
You have bought the nothing which I sell.

In casting out what is not to His Likeness
You are transformed to Him.
Grace alone brings you to Union with the
Bridegroom."

Then I looked into the eyes of that man. Within them was that light which shone in the eyes of Jacob at Penuel after he had wrestled all night.'[72]

***

John pondered a while. His Master's visions painted the desert path. For:

Only through the silences in the desert wastes
did a monk understand himself.
Only in battles against what pleased the body and
the spirit, could he purify himself.
Only in nakedness of spirit could he receive
that God who ever comes to the lowly and poor.

Thus it was that John understood that his Master had glimpsed the Shekhinah, the Glory in which the Loving Father dwells.[73]

But to all who received him… he gave power
to become children of God.

(John 1:12)

22
Faith

Thy word is a lamp to my feet,
and a light unto my path.
(Ps 119:105)

John welcomed the dusty traveller into the courtyard. Having washed his feet, he offered fresh water from the well and then took him into his cell for a simple meal. The stooped body and ageing face were familiar.

'You and the Abbot last gave me hospitality two years ago, when I travelled with friends to Arsinoe. My name is Sarmatas and I am a teacher from Alexandria.'

John quickly remembered the modest scholar. Then he explained that Nicholas was sick and would not be able to talk with him. Smiling, Sarmatas slowly replied:

'But wise fathers have wise sons. Does it matter to the poor donkey whether it is the father or the son who lifts his burden?'

After they had said the psalms and prayers for the hour, they sat together in silence.

***

Then Sarmatas explained to the Dwarf that he was travelling to Scete. He intended to join the brothers there and devote himself to a life of solitude in the desert.

'You, who were taught by the wise Ammonius himself, do you now give up your knowledge, set aside your students, take leave of your friends and bid farewell to wealth and home?' asked John.

'Should I place before God a cluster of dates when He desires olives? There is no advantage in a life which gives what He does not seek.'

'How did this perception arise within you?' queried John.

Sarmatas was silent for a while. Then hesitantly, he spoke:

'A while ago I met in the streets of Alexandria an old woman who earned enough pence to live by taking in washing. I helped to carry her load and as we walked I asked this question: "Do you believe in that Trinity which is the Father, the Son, and the Holy Spirit?" She answered in a whisper, with head bowed and eyes seeking the lowliest part of the road:

"Holy Master, I have no letters and am without understanding of that dread Truth. My life is this:

I wash the shirt of a potter who brings form and
beauty to shapeless clay.
I lave the silken tunic of an architect who plans
great buildings on fine goatskin.
I clean the birth cloths of a midwife who awakens
the Creator's living gift."

Thus I saw that God the Father was ever born as she cherished her part in His Creation.

She went on:

"I give alms to the sick beggar who lies at the
city's gate.
I sit through each night caring for my friend as life
ebbs away from her.
I seek to bring reconciliation to my neighbours that
enemies may be friends again."

Thus I saw that Christ the Son was ever born in she who was an instrument in His redemptive task.

She went on:

> "My endeavour is to bring to those who are put within my way:
>
> A dagger to sever the strap that binds their freedom;
> An axe to break the yoke that crushes their joy;
> A dart to pierce the helm that hides peace from them."

Thus I saw that the Holy Spirit was ever born as she went her loving way doing His work. It was in this way that I perceived that she who demurred from knowledge of that Blessed Trinity yet lived her life wholly within its compass.

The faith of this laundry woman of Alexandria showed me that the sum of my learning and all my teaching has been but the building of a grand gate to a courtyard through which I have never walked. Now I begin the journey. Show me the way, little brother.'

There was a long pause. John was moved by the sincerity of his speech and the depth of his sacrifice. He spoke simply:

> 'Thus it is with me too.
>
> Faith is a trust which a child has for her mother.
> It is a joyous remembrance of the time of a father's presence.
> It is a celebration that the Day Star from on high comes to us.[74]
>
> Reason and logic are the least of its servants for:
>
> Faith is the creature's reply to the Creator's question.
> It rises from awe:

At the hush of the desert;
At the kiss of earth and sky on a far horizon;
At the coming of His servant Death to take us home.
Faith is the believer's echo of His Spirit's song.

The way you must go is the way you already know.
He has set it in your heart.
The solitude will speak to you.'

***

They embraced as two brothers who shared the same treasure. And after a night's lodging Sarmatas continued his journey to Scete.

***

He wakens... wakens my ear to hear as those who are taught.
(Isaiah 50:4)

23
The Way

For the Lord knows the way of the righteous...
(Ps 1:6)

'Though you do not know me, I know of you', said the traveller mysteriously as he ate the figs offered by Nicholas. He was a short man not yet in the middle of life. A fine linen shirt and a cloak of expensive wool clearly proclaimed a Roman of noble birth.

'My name is Lucius. I am the younger brother to Markus Marius, centurion of the Governor's Guard, torn by the beasts at the Circus. My father was the Tribune Gaius Marius, who fought in Gaul.'

John and the Abbot looked thoughtfully at each other and listened as Lucius told them of his father's death. A mathematician and administrator, he had acted as Gaius' secretary and steward. Though a younger son, by the death of Markus, rich family estates that banked the River Tiber[75] were now his.

***

'Great was the wealth that Gaius bequeathed. But a greater was given by Markus', said Lucius.

He explained that his brother had shared his new faith in secret and that his own heart had been slowly moved by its truth. Telling this to his father, as vitality waned and death approached, the tribune had laughed, saying:

'Is not the desert of history strewn with the carcasses of

stinking religions? Do the conceits of a Nazarene[76] match the reasoning of Athens or the oratory of Rome?'

Yet he had asked Lucius to promise that, should he wish to espouse the new Christian philosophy, he would seek teaching from Nicholas. 'For his flame burns as deeply as mine. And I have felt its heat', he had said.

So Lucius stayed with Nicholas and John for some months.

* * *

Nicholas said: 'What is in your heart? Do you leave all for the desert? Do you return to your lands by the Tiber's shore?'

He replied:

> 'If a baker destroys his oven, can he feed the hungry?
> If a weaver breaks his loom, can he clothe the naked?
> If a physician picks no herbs, can he heal the sick?

So I shall go to Rome and steward my estates. Thus may I serve the needs of orphans and widows. Thus may I minister to those whose bodies are racked and whose minds are crazed.'

Nicholas said to him: 'If that is the way you walk, it has five gates.

> The first is opened, for already
> You have seen in the outwardness of the world, the indwelling of His Spirit;
> You have heard Him call your name in the winds which thresh the desert sands.

Only those who are naked will open the second gate.
Regard not that clothing which the world gives.

Your estates are but a clod on the Lord's sandal.
Your authority but a morning mist awaiting the sun.
Though you have many possessions, prize them not.

Rise early. Dress simply. Eat frugally. Be abstemious.
Conduct your business as a steward for His Master.
Meet the needs of the wretched. Love the brethren.[77]

Only those who can die will open the third gate.
Be blind to those towers in which men hide for safety.

Truth is stranger than great learning.
It is deeper than human philosophy.
It is not found in bodily desire or spiritual craving.

You will wake in darkness without sight of the track.
Great fears will swoop about your head. Your staff will snap.
You will stumble under sucking waters.
In your drowning you will say, "He has hidden Himself."

Only for those who are reborn will the fourth gate open.
Step within it and wait. He brings what He will.
Know this that what He gives is without limit or bound.

If He brings light, walk in faith to its Furthest End.

If He brings pain take it with hope. It is a Son's
Way.
If He brings mystery, seek Love at its very Heart.

Should He pour for you the wine of
pomegranates: Drink.
Should He take a towel and wash your body:
Rejoice.
Should He fasten a cloak about your neck:
Embrace Him.
And the fifth gate?
That is His dearest treasure, given only to His
own.
It cannot be named for it is sweeter than all words.

Can that ecstasy of love
In which one life is welcomed by All Life;
In which one song is encircled by All Singing;
In which one soul is girdled with Eternal Life;
Be set down in letters?

It is a poem which only His Tongue can utter
And the ears of those whom He has blessed
receive.'

***

'Each second year at the time of the Autumn rains, I shall journey from Rome to Nitria for your counsel', said Lucius as he bade farewell to his hosts.

Watching the sand of the desert envelop him, John said to the Abbot: 'I fear for him in Rome. Will he follow the Way?'

'If the mother sparrow does not thrust her young from the nest, will they fly? His will is steadfast for he knows that he lives now not only for himself but for Markus too. And perhaps a little for Gaius. He carries letters to the Church in Rome. There are many there who will light his path', replied Nicholas. But John caught the hesitancy in his voice.

> We were buried ...with him ...into death ...so that as Christ was raised ...we too might walk in newness of life.
>
> (Romans 6:4)

24
Guilt

He has made me dwell in darkness... He has walled me about... He has put heavy chains on me... He shuts out my prayer... My soul is bereft of peace, I have forgotten what happiness is.

(Lamentations 3:6,7,8,17)

But two miles from their cells, Nicholas and John were hurrying to avoid the sandstorm building on the eastern horizon. They heard a groan. Then both stumbled forwards over a dust-strewn body. They tended the stranger gently. A well-built man, still in his prime, his lips were cracked and tongue already swollen. Without a flask, he was dying of thirst.

'What traveller of these parts journeys without water?' said John to the Abbot, as he poured a few drops from his own flask into the dry mouth.

But the answer came from the stranger in a barely audible whisper, 'One who wishes to die.'

***

John lit candles, for the storm extinguished the sun and brought a strange darkness to the cell. For a night and a day they nursed the traveller and sat with him. Eventually he was well enough to speak.

'Your kindness is misplaced, good brothers. I wish that you had left me in those drear wastes. I sought death and thought I caught his breath. Too soon you came.'

'Many seek death in the desert and finding it come to new birth', said Nicholas very quietly.

'The death I seek is the crumbling of my body to its dust. Only this can quench my guilt', he said becoming very agitated.

'Friend, is your guilt so great that it cannot be lifted?'

'Those who might raise it are gone from me forever.' He wept.

He was exhausted again. John and the Abbot made him comfortable and withdrew to say their office.

> My eyes flow with rivers of tears because of the destruction of the daughter of my people.
>
> (Lamentations 3:48)

***

It was not until the third day that he walked without stumbling and spoke again of the shadow that stretched over his life.

'I have four children, three sons and the youngest a daughter. In giving birth to her my wife died. The sons grew strong and happily shared my work. My daughter smilingly learned the household tasks. She wove our shirts and baked our bread. Possessed of a beauty and likeness to her mother, as she grew in years my flesh was troubled. One evening when she was but sixteen, we celebrated the natal day of her eldest brother with new wine, though she drank but little. Later when her brothers were heavily asleep, the ache of my flesh drove me to her room. There, despite her weeping and ignoring her pleading, I lay with her. Immediately I found that she was not a virgin. I let my lust take its course. Then in great anger I beat her requiring the name of her lover. It was a young monk to whom she went for payment of our account. Each week we sent fresh vegetables to the monastery. Each week their love had grown stronger. When she told me that she was with child by him, my rage spilled over and I put her from the house, wishing never to see her again.'

With head hanging low, his lament ended in a hoarse whisper. 'I am a farmer from Cellia. My name is Arminion. She whom I have so terribly treated is Sarah. She bears a child by a monk, young Pinufius of Cellia. Help me, Father, what may I do?'

***

Nicholas embraced him gently about the shoulders, waited until the sobbing ceased, then sitting with him said:

'My son, forgiveness is a deeper river than you know.

> Did not Stephen the deacon,[78] before he fell asleep, cry mercy from God for those who threw rocks to kill him?
> Did not a son of Joseph the carpenter,[79] as he died, seek excusal for those who drove nails through his fists?

Your forgiveness lies in three parts:

> First, seek forgiveness from God.
>
> Though you have broken His ancient taboo, He will not accept your life for this sin.
>
> > Turn from the shadows. Go to Cellia. Love His children.
> > Give half the income from your farm to those about you:
> > > That the sick may receive a physician;

That the hungry and thirsty may be relieved;
That the unjustly oppressed may be delivered;
And those who are naked, clothed.
Do this as long as God gives you life.

Second, seek forgiveness from yourself.

Your guilt is a sickening monster whose shape ever changes.
She pursues you down the greasy steps of endless passages where all is final blackness and filthy stench.
Stop. Turn. Face the dreaded thing. Step slowly towards her.
Know the pain. Hear the words about your incest and cruelty.
Walk deeply into this torment. Acknowledge the wrong.
Thus may your heart forgive.
Thus may your life be renewed.

Third, seek forgiveness from Sarah.

It is His Providence that John can find her.
He will be your tongue and bear your gifts for restitution.
If she forgives this ancient wrong of mankind, he will hear.
If she suffers too deeply, he will accord time for healing.
Whatever span you wait for this forgiveness:
Stay in hope with much prayer;
Accept the hurt – it is just;
Endure it – yet let it not degrade.
Forge no more links in this chain of pain.

Joy may be your unexpected harvest.'

***

‘He will reach Cellia in time to help with the ploughing’, said John as Arminion, now chastened and restored, journeyed home.

‘I wonder how long he will cloak the truth from his sons?’ mused Nicholas, partly to John, partly to himself and partly to the blowing wind of the desert.

25
Bishop

I will instruct you...
with my eye upon you.
(Ps 32:8)

Of the group approaching through the desert John's sharp eye remembered Thomas and Theon, priests to the Bishop of Alexandria. The others, perhaps eight, perhaps ten, walking gravely and without speech among themselves, seemed older. Their donkey carried provisions though they gladly drank the fresh water offered by the Abbot and his disciple. After they had washed the feet of their visitors, they prayed with them.

Thomas and Theon, explaining that they were but guides and servants in this company, introduced each person. John was surprised for it seemed that the most senior, the most learned and the most holy priests in all of Alexandria, had come to the desert. But as he looked at his Master, he recognised a mirth which was scarcely beneath the surface of his voice.

'Brothers,' the Abbot queried, 'why is the jewel of Alexandria's Christianity now set within these crumbling bricks?' They smiled at his jest.

Then Timothy the Good, who cared for lepers and those poor without eyes at the city gates, spoke for them.

'Nicholas the Holy, you who understand the silences of our God and know His Secret Wisdom, we bring news which concerns you. Our Master Simon, Bishop in Alexandria, died nine months ago.'

'That was given to us from our gathering at the weekly Synaxis', said Nicholas. 'At each evening prayer we speak thanks for the simple goodness of his life and pray for his soul.'

Timothy nodded: 'There is another matter. The Church in Alexandria has sent us to you with letters. Their substance is this. You are nominated successor to Simon. You are called to be Bishop in Alexandria. That is the agreed desire of all the brethren.'

John heard no further what Timothy said and the others said. His mind spun so many thoughts. He only gave attention again as Nicholas spoke, requesting his visitors to remain for one day and night in the desert, while he sought God's will before giving them answer.

> Thou hast turned for me my mourning into
> dancing...
> that my soul may praise thee and not be silent.
>
> (Ps 30:11,12)

***

John attended to the needs of their guests while Nicholas went one half-day's travel to a quiet place. It was not until the third day that he returned. After he had refreshed himself, everyone gathered around him. Giving courteous thanks, he said:

'Good friends, the prize you bring is guarded by three walls.

> The first is a wall of ignorance.
> Has a wandering poet from Gaul the wit to rule
> in Rome?
> No more have I the aptness to govern in Alexandria.'

'Against your innocence we offer our experience', they said.

'The second is a wall of poverty.
Does a beggar hold court in an emperor's palace?
No more have I riches for this service.'

'Against your need we offer our wealth', they said.

'The third is a wall of age.
Will the crooked, grey with years, compete in the Games?
No more have I vigour for this labour.'

'To stay your fatigue we offer our support', they said.

Then Timothy the Good spoke:

'In this office:
Your back will not stoop with outward cargo.
Your shoulders will not carry heavy vesture.

We seek a lord whose wisdom knows that:
What is within reach, is beyond our grasp;
What is within sight, is beyond our vision;
What is within hearing, is beyond our understanding.

We seek a Bishop to guide us to:
The radiance of the Father's Being;
The glory of the Resurrected Son;
The mystery of the Spirit's Presence.'

Nicholas said:

'The lord you seek is already within your city.
When it was said to him: "Where is the radiance of the Father's Being?" he showed
Pink blossom on the almond tree; babe at a mother's breast.
When it was said to him: "Where is the glory of the Resurrected Son?" he showed

Scented grasses in a darkened night; lovers' sacrifice.
When it was said to him: "Where is the mystery of the Spirit's Presence?" he showed
The least grain of wheat; a woman forgotten, dying alone.'

'Who is he?' they asked.

'He is one who has broken the wall of ignorance, for he knows Alexandria and its citizens well.
He is one who has broken the wall of poverty, for he is heir to great estates.
He is one who has broken the wall of age, for his vigour still grows.
As I tell you his name remember:
It was to a child, Samuel, that the Lord came and stood.
It was from the mouths of babes that wisdom was poured.
It is only as children we shall enter His Kingdom.

Living in the great monastery at Alexandria, under the guardianship of the Blessed Bessarion, is one whom the Spirit has kissed. Where others walk slowly for spiritual discernment, he flies quick as an arrow to the target's ring. Barely two decades old, yet wise beyond his years, he is grandson to Xanthias, Senior in the School of Rhetoric. Twin to Syncletica, his name is Rufinus.'

***

'Will they make Rufinus their Bishop?' asked John, as he and the Abbot watched them all set out sadly for Alexandria.

'When did heavenly foolishness ever touch earthly wisdom?' laughed Nicholas. Then the Abbot and the Dwarf were once again enveloped amid the sands of silence.

Notes

1 The Nitrian desert lies about 40 miles south of Alexandria and 50 miles west of Cairo. It takes its name from the *natron* (soda) which was collected there.

2 The Synaxis was a meeting which could be for prayer or the celebration of the Eucharist.

3 Ps 119:30 is quoted from the *Book of Common Prayer*.

4 'This thought traps...' *See* L. Wittgenstein, *Philosophical Investigations* 1, 1968, Section 115, p. 48e. 'A picture held us captive.'

5 Scete lies 40 miles south of Nitria.

6 In the Old Testament the Leviathan is a crocodile or a whale.

7 Arsinoe lies 50 miles south west of Cairo.

8 By the third century AD Alexandria was a flourishing Christian centre.

9 Pispir lies 25 miles to the east of Arsinoe.

10 The apophatic way and the kataphatic are respectively the negative and the positive ways of knowing God and of praying. The first would hold that God is not love because humans can only know what *they* mean by love, which is a limited concept. God, however, is not limited and is in all respects limitless. The second would say that God is love because he causes love.

11 'The Lord Christ... the Universal Word...' This is an idea well used by Christian apologists. It occurs in the second century AD in Justin Martyr's *Apology* (46,1-4) and in the twentieth century in Karl Rahner's *Theological Investigations*, vol. 12, chap. 9, and vol. 17, chap. 5.

12 Heraclitus was a distinguished Greek philosopher who lived in Ephesus, Asia Minor, about 500 BC, Philo was a Jewish philosopher of Alexandria who lived ca. 20 BC – ca. 50 AD.

13 'scarlet beast...' Revelation 17:3.

14 'Shulammite...' Song of Solomon 6:13. The girl of Shulam creates a problem for commentators since Shulam is unknown. The most popular suggestions are that it means Shunem, a town near Jesreel on the plain of Esdraelon, or that repointing the Hebrew it means either 'Solomon's girl' or 'the perfect one'.

15 'Pools of Heshbon.' Song of Solomon 7:4. These are reservoirs for storing water and have been excavated on the ancient site of Heshbon which is near Amman in Jordan.

16 There is a long history of canon law on nocturnal emissions. The more severe view simply forbids communion after an emission. Sometimes a distinction is made between an emission suffered after deliberate dalliance with desire for a woman and one caused by demonic temptation. Some authors consider an emission to be a natural excretion and not a sin.

17 'In solitude one is united to all...' The doctrine of 'solitudo pluralis', of corporate solitude, is central to the eremitical tradition in Christianity. See St Peter Damian, *Selected Writings on the Spiritual Life*, Faber, 1959, p. 57, and Thomas Merton, *No Man Is An Island*, Burns & Oates, 1955, p. 219.

18 Lake Mareotis lies to the north east of the Nitrian desert and to the east of Alexandria.

19 'Jacob wrestled.' Genesis 32:24.

20 The Jabbok is a stream which runs into the River Jordan mid-way between the Sea of Galilee and the Dead Sea.

21 Quoted from the *Book of Common Prayer*.

22 'White lilies, sweet jasmine and... the myrtle tree.' The myrtle is an ancient symbol of love, the white colour and sweet scent of the jasmine symbolise grace and the lily is a symbol of purity closely associated with the Virgin Mary.

23 Astarte was a virgin goddess of love in whose temples and in whose honour prostitution was practised.

24 '...nameless concubine of Bethlehem.' P. Tribble, *Texts of Terror*, Fortress Press, 1984, chap. 3 gives a challenging but harrowing account of this incident.

25 'Zachary says...' is a reference to Zechariah 1:8. The myrtle is interpreted by some Christians as an allusion to the Gentiles con-

verted by Christ. So in this passage Christ rides among the Gentiles followed by martyrs and confessors.

26 'an argument from pictures...' Within formal logic no argument by analogy is ever valid in the sense of having a conclusion which follows from the premises with a logical necessity. Analogical argument is only more or less probable though it can have cogency.

27 'Aldebaran... Hyades'. The Pleiades is a galactic cluster found in the constellation Taurus. Aldebaran is the brightest star in that constellation.

28 Behemoth. In the Book of Job (40:15-24) this is usually understood as a reference to the hippopotamus.

29 Cellia was 75 miles south of Alexandria.

30 '...descent into Hell.' In Acts 2:31, Ephesians 4:9-10 and 1 Peter 3:19-20 the New Testament teaches that Christ descended to Hell after the crucifixion. It was a belief of the very early Church that there he continued his work of reconciliation and redemption.

31 '...plane tree... white violets.' The plane is a straight tree whose branches are high and wide. So it is a symbol of firmness of character and moral superiority. Violets symbolise the humility of the Virgin Mary and also that of the Son of God in assuming human form at the Incarnation.

32 Vandals. Germanic groups of tribes who threatened the Roman Empire in the fourth and fifth centuries.

33 Goths. Germanic tribes who harried the Roman Empire between the third and the fifth centuries.

34 Homer. A Greek epic poet ca. 700 BC.

35 Scythians. Peoples who lived at the northern borders of the Black Sea. They were eventually absorbed by the Goths.

36 Stoic. The Stoic philosophers took their name from the Painted Stoa or Colonnade in Athens where Zeno, the founder of the School, taught at the end of the fourth century BC.

37 Zion. Originally a hill of ancient Jerusalem, it signifies for Christians their Heavenly City.

38 Pentecost. The seventh Sunday after Easter. It commemorates the giving of the Holy Spirit to the Jerusalem Church.

39 Myrrh, aloes and cassia. These are aromatic woods. Ophir was a place from which the choicest gold came. Its location is disputed.

40 Orange trees. Its white flowers suggest purity and so they are a traditional adornment of Christian brides.

41 Pomegranates. A symbol, because of its many seeds, of fertility.

42 Ichabod. 1 Samuel 4:21. Son of Phineas and grandson of Eli, his name means 'No Glory'. As his dying mother gave birth to him, news came of the loss of the Ark. Thus she called her son Ichabod.

43 Jannes and Jambres. Exodus 7:11ff and 2 Timothy 3:8. Two Egyptian magicians who opposed the miracles of Moses. Tradition credits them with planting an earthly Paradise in the desert.

44 Immanuel. Isaiah 7:14 and Matthew 1:23.

45 Liar, Tempter, Prince of this World: all refer to Satan.

46 The literature of the Desert Fathers emphasises the frequency with which those who fasted and were celibate dreamed of rich food and sensual delights.

47 Daniel and Anoub. Under the Emperors Valentinian and Valens there was conscription of monks for military service.

48 Lattices of heaven. Early Israel believed that small apertures in the sky could be opened to give rain and dew (e.g. Genesis 7:11).

49 Psalms – the habitation of Christ. From very early times Christians have found in the Psalms, and many other Old Testament passages, a witness to the Messiah. The early Fathers took the Psalter and explained it as a prophecy about Christ and his Church.

50 My terrible tale. This is a re-telling of the sotry of the unknown concubine of Bethlehem in the Book of Judges. I have added names but little else. Where there were alternative readings I have chosen what made best sense to me. In Judges 19:2 the Bible follows the Masoretic and Syriac Texts giving 'his concubine played the whore against him' (Authorised Version). The Greek and Old Latin Texts give 'his concubine became angry with him' which seems to allow the words I have chosen for the story. P Tribble, *op cit*.

51 Jebus is Jerusalem.

52 Judges 19:25b. Quoted from the New International Version of the Bible.

53 'Paul'. Romans 2:14-15.

54 'Our Lord Himself'. Luke 12:57.

55 Cush is Ethiopia (e.g. AV marginal reading Genesis 2:13) and Erech is the second city of Nimrod (Genesis 10:10).

56 No-Amon is the city of Thebes in Egypt (Nahum 3:8).

57 Bozrah is a city of Edom (Jeremiah 49:22) and Heshbon is a city of the Amorites and the Moabites (Numbers 21:25-28).

58 A Scribe is a Jewish scholar who interpreted and taught the Scriptures. They are regarded as doctors of the Law.

59 'The vines of Sodom...' Deuteronomy 32:32-33.

60 'Drink wine...' Daniel 1:1-16). Gentiles usually poured an offering to their God(s) when they drank wine.

61 'What crawls or creeps...' Leviticus 11:21-22 exempts locusts from the prohibition on 'flying creeping things that have four feet'.

62 Cheese and fowl together. Deuteronomy 14:21 is the basis for this prohibition.

63 'A place where any other has died...' Numbers 19:11-22 deals with corpse impurity.

64 'Any bodily discharge...' Leviticus 15:2-15 deals with impurity caused by genital discharge. A male with such discharge causes secondary impurity by what he touches.

65 'The School to which...' There was a School whose understanding of the Law was flexible.

66 Ruach is a Hebrew word which can mean 'spirit'.

67 'House of Bread' in Hebrew is Bethlehem.

68 'From the womb...', 'He will drink...' and 'Sit at...' are phrases from Psalm 110. This psalm is quoted more frequently in the New

Testament than any other. The early Church as well as the New Testament writers took it for granted that it was written by King David and that is concerned the Messiah.

69 Moses and the Burning Bush. Exodus 3:2.

70 Beelzebub: a pagan deity, a Lord of Evil Spirits.

71 Abraham at a mountain in the Land of Moriah. Genesis 22:1-14.

72 Jacob at Penuel. Genesis 32:24.

73 Shekhinah is the visible splendour of the Divine Presence. Occasionally used as a periphrasis for God, it is to some Christians symbolic of the Incarnation.

74 Day Star is a symbol for Christ (2 Peter 1:19).

75 Tiber: the river which runs through Rome.

76 Nazarene: refers to Jesus of Nazareth.

77 The brethren: other Christians.

78 Stephen the deacon. Acts 7:60.

79 A son of Joseph, i.e., Jesus. Luke 23:34.

Select Bibliography

This bibliography only contains those books which helped me to reflect on my own experience of the desert. They created an atmosphere within which interpretation, understanding and subsequent writing took place.

1. The Desert Way

A.M. Allchin, *Solitude and Communion,* Fairacres, 1977.
D. Chitty, *The Desert a City*, Oxford, 1966.
A Louth, *The Wilderness of God*, Darton, Longman & Todd, 1991.
J.P. Migne, Relevant volumes in the *Patrologia Graeca* and the *Patrologia Latina.*
T. Merton, *Bread in the Wilderness*, Catholic Book Club, 1953. *No Man is an Island*, Burns & Oates, 1955. *The Wisdom of the Desert*, New Directions, 1960. *Thoughts in Solitude*, Burns & Oates, 1958.
A. Pronzato, *Meditations on the Sand*, St Paul Publications, 1982.
N. Russell (Trans.), *The Lives of the Desert Fathers*, Mowbray, 1980.
H. Waddell (Trans.), *The Desert Fathers*, Fontana, 1962.
B. Ward (Trans.), *The Sayings of the Desert Fathers*, Mowbray, 1981.

2. Stories and Storytelling

A.J. Band, *Nahman of Bratislay: The Tales*, Paulist Press, 1978.
W.J. Bausch, *Storytelling, Imagination and Faith*, Twenty-Third Publications, 1984.
M. Buber, *The Origin and Meaning of Hasidism*, Harper, 1966.
M. Buber, *Hasidism and Modern Man*, Harper, 1966.
Y. Eliach, *Hasidic Tales of the Holocaust*, Vintage Books, 1988.
The Treasured Writings of Kahlil Gibran, Castle Books, 1980.
D.J. O'Leary, *Windows of Wonder*, Paulist Press, 1991.
A. de Mello, *The Song of the Bird*, Gujarat Sahitya Prakash, Anand, 1982.
A. de Mello, *Wellsprings*, Gujarat Sahitya Prakash, Anand, 1984.
J. Ribes, *Parables and Fables for Modern Man*, St Paul Publications, 1990.
I. Shah, *Wisdom of the Idiots*, Dutton, 1971.
I. Shah, *Thinkers of the East*, Penguin, 1971.

J. Shea, *Stories of God*, Thomas More Press, 1978.
J. Shea, *Stories of Faith*, Thomas More Press, 1980.
P. Tribble, *Texts of Terror*, Fortress Press, 1984.
E. Wiesel, *Souls on Fire and Somewhere a Master*, Penguin, 1984.

POETRY

J. Ashbery, *Selected Poems*, Paladin, 1987.
C.P. Cavafy, *Collected Poems*, Chatto & Windus, 1979.
A. Gregor, *Selected Poems*, Doubleday & Co, 1971.
E. Jennings, *Collected Poems*, Carcanet, 1986.
D. Jones, *The Anathemata*, Faber & Faber, 1972.
R. McKuen, *Come to Me in Silence*, W.H. Allen, 1974.
G. Shaw, *Seeds of Love*, Fairacres, 1978.
R.S. Thomas, *Counterpoint*, Bloodaxe Books, 1990.
R.S. Thomas, *Later Poems 1972-1982*, Papermac, 1985.
R.S. Thomas, *Selected Poems 1946-1968*, Bloodaxe Books, 1986.